STILL STEAMING

A Guide to Britain's Standard Gauge Heritage Railways 2019-2020

EDITOR
Steve Askew

Twenty-third Edition

RAILWAY LOCATOR MAP

The numbers shown on this map relate to the page numbers for each railway. Pages 5-6 contain an alphabetical listing of the railways featured in this guide. Please note that the markers on this map show the approximate location only.

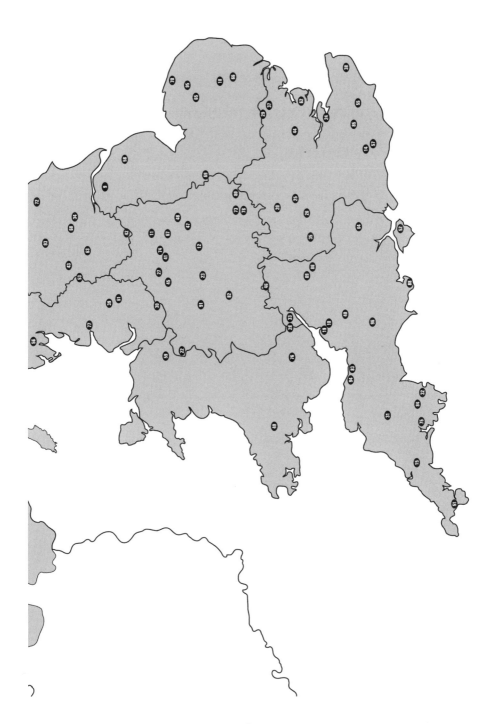

3

FOREWORD & ACKNOWLEDGEMENTS

We were greatly impressed by the friendly and cooperative manner of the staff and helpers of the railways which we selected to appear in this book, and wish to thank them for the help they have given. In addition we wish to thank Bob Budd (cover design) and Michael Robinson (page layouts) for their help and also Jonathan James who has provided us with photographs for several railways.

Although we believe that the information contained in this guide is accurate at the time of going to press, we, and the Railways and Museums itemised, are unable to accept liability for any loss, damage, distress or injury suffered as a result of any inaccuracies. Furthermore, we and the Railways are unable to guarantee operating and opening times which may always be subject to cancellation without notice.

We realise that other UK Standard Gauge railways are operating or about to resume operating and we hope to include them in a future edition of Still Steaming.

If you feel we should include other locations or information in future editions, please let us know so that we may give them consideration. We would like to thank you for buying this guide and wish you 'Happy Steaming'!

Steve Askew
EDITOR

Note: Further copies of our railway guides, Still Steaming, Little Puffers and Tiny Trains may be obtained, post free, from our address below or ordered on-line via our web site –

www.soccer-books.co.uk

British Library Cataloguing in Publication Data
A catalogue record for this book is available from the British Library

ISBN-13:   978-1-86223-398-0

Copyright © 2019, SOCCER BOOKS LIMITED. (01472 696226)
72 St. Peter's Avenue, Cleethorpes, N.E. Lincolnshire, DN35 8HU, England

Manufactured in the UK by TJ International Ltd.

COVER PICTURE

The cover image was taken at the Aln Valley Railway during July 2018 and shows No. 60, a Hunslet Austerity 0-6-0 saddle tank at Lionheart Station in Alnwick.

CONTENTS

ALDERNEY RAILWAY

Address: P.O. Box 1075, Alderney, Channel Islands   GY9 3DA
Telephone Nº: 07911 739572
Year Formed: 1978
Location of Line: Braye Harbour to Mannez Quarry, Alderney
Length of Line: 2 miles

Nº of Steam Locos: None at present
Nº of Other Locos: 2
Nº of Members: 50
Annual Membership Fee: £15.00
Approx Nº of Visitors P.A.: 2,000+
Gauge: Standard
Web site: www.alderneyrailway.com

Photo courtesy of David Staines

GENERAL INFORMATION

Nearest Mainline Station: Not applicable
Nearest Bus Station: Not applicable
Car Parking: Available on site
Coach Parking: Available on site
Souvenir Shop(s): Yes
Food & Drinks: None at the Railway itself but available nearby

SPECIAL INFORMATION

The original line was built during the 1840s to assist in the construction of the large breakwater in Braye Harbour and fortifications on the island.
The line itself opened in 1847 and was the first nationalised railway run by the Admiralty.

OPERATING INFORMATION

Opening Times: Every Sunday from 1st April 2019 until September and also on Saturdays in July and August. An Easter Special operates as does a Santa Special. Please contact the railway for further information. Trains usually run at 2.30pm and 3.30pm although Santa Specials run 15 minutes earlier.
Steam Working: None at present
Prices: Adult Return £5.00
Child Return £3.00

Detailed Directions:
The Railway is situated adjacent to Braye Harbour.

ALN VALLEY RAILWAY

Address: Lionheart Station, Lionheart Enterprise Park, Alnwick NE66 2EX	**No of Steam Locos**: 3
Information Line No: 0300 030-3311	**No of Other Locos**: 5
Year Formed: 1995	**No of Members**: 400 approximately
Location: Alnwick, Northumberland	**Approx No of Visitors P.A.**: 12,000
Length: 1,700 metres (just over 1 mile)	**Gauge**: Standard
	Web site: www.alnvalleyrailway.co.uk

GENERAL INFORMATION

Nearest Mainline Station: Alnmouth (5 miles)
Nearest Bus Station: Alnwick (1½ miles)
Car Parking: Available on site
Coach Parking: Available
Souvenir Shop(s): Yes
Food & Drinks: Available

SPECIAL INFORMATION

The Aln Valley Railway Trust plans to re-open the branch line from Alnmouth station, located on the Edinburgh–London main line, through to Alnwick, primarily as a heritage railway attraction. The track has already been laid for over half this distance, including over the seven-arch Cawledge Viaduct.

OPERATING INFORMATION

Opening Times: 2019 dates: Sundays, Bank Holiday Saturdays and Mondays from 6th April to 29th September (plus 26th & 27th October). Open from 10.30am to 4.30pm on operating days.
Steam Working: 6th, 7th, 20th, 21st & 22nd April; 4th, 5th, 6th, 25th, 26th & 27th May; 1st, 2nd, 15th & 16th June; 7th, 27th & 28th July; Saturdays and Sundays in August; 1st, 14th, 15th, 28th & 29th September; 28th, 29th & 30th December. Santa Specials run on 7th, 8th, 11th, 14th, 15th, 21st & 22nd December (pre-booking required)
Prices: Adult Day Ticket £6.00
Child Day Ticket £2.00 (Under-5s free)
Family Day Ticket £14.00

Detailed Directions by Car:
Exit the A1 at Willowburn Junction (just to the south of Alnwick) and follow the brown tourist signs marked "Aln Valley Railway" through the Enterprise Park to Lionheart Station. (SatNav users select NE66 2HT)
Buses to and from Alnwick Bus Station (services 472 and X15) stop by the Willowburn Filling Station/Sainsbury's store just to the north of the A1. Follow the brown tourist signs on foot from here for the railway.

APPLEBY FRODINGHAM R.P.S.

Address: Appleby Frodingham Railway Preservation Society, c/o Tourist Information Centre, The Buttercross, Market Place, Brigg DN20 8ER **Telephone Nº**: (01652) 657053 (bookings) **Year Formed**: 1990 **Location of Line**: British Steel, Scunthorpe	**Length of Line**: 15 miles used on tours from almost 100 miles of track **Nº of Steam Locos**: 5 **Nº of Other Locos**: 3 **Nº of Members**: 60 **Gauge**: Standard **Web site**: www.afrps.co.uk

GENERAL INFORMATION

Nearest Mainline Station: Scunthorpe (1 mile)
Nearest Bus Station: Scunthorpe (½ mile)
Car Parking: Large free car park at the site
Coach Parking: At the site
Souvenir Shop(s): Yes – at the Loco Shed
Food & Drinks: Available at the Loco Shed

SPECIAL INFORMATION

The Society operates 15 mile Rail and Brake Van tours of the Scunthorpe steelworks site (which covers almost 12 square miles) using its extensive internal railway system.

OPERATING INFORMATION

Opening Times: Selected weekends throughout the year which <u>must</u> be pre-booked via (01652) 657053 or e-mail – brigg.tic@northlincs.gov.uk
Private Hire of a train is now available for parties and anniversaries with use of the Lounge coach.
Steam Working: Most active days. Ask for further details when booking.
Prices: Free – but the society relies on donations which are collected at the end of each tour.
Please note that children cannot be carried on Brake Van tours due to the open verandahs.
(Phone 01652 659108 with any enquiries)

Detailed Directions by Car:
Exit the M180 at Junction 4 and take the A18 into Scunthorpe. Turn right at the roundabout by Morrisons supermarket and follow Brigg Road for approximately ½ mile. Turn right into Gate E. Car parking is available on the left and the path to the station is on the right.   SatNav users please enter: DN16 1XA

AVON VALLEY RAILWAY

Address: Bitton Station, Bath Road, Bitton, Bristol BS30 6HD
Telephone Nº: (0117) 932-5538
Year Formed: 1973
Location of Line: Midway between Bristol and Bath on A431
Length of Line: 3 miles

Nº of Steam Locos: 6
Nº of Other Locos: 5
Nº of Members: Approximately 700
Annual Membership Fee: £15.00
Approx Nº of Visitors P.A.: 80,000
Gauge: Standard
Web site: www.avonvalleyrailway.org
E-mail: info@avonvalleyrailway.org

GENERAL INFORMATION

Nearest Mainline Station: Keynsham (1½ miles)
Nearest Bus Station: Bristol or Bath (7 miles)
Car Parking: Available at Bitton Station
Coach Parking: Available at Bitton Station
Souvenir Shop(s): Yes
Food & Drinks: Yes

SPECIAL INFORMATION

The line originally opened in 1869 as a direct route from Birmingham to the south coast but was axed in the 1960s following the Beeching Report. Three miles of track has now been re-laid along the Bristol to Bath section of the line.

OPERATING INFORMATION

Opening Times: 2019 dates: Every Saturday and Sunday and Bank Holiday Monday, from April to September (but for the first Saturday of the month), plus selected Wednesdays from May to September. Also open on Sundays in October and from Tuesday to Thursday during the school summer and half-term holidays. Also open for Santa Specials in December. Open 10.30am to 5.00pm. Please check the web site for further details.
Steam Working: 11.00am to 4.00pm on most days
Prices: Adult £7.50 (£8.50 on Steam Days)
Child £5.50 (£6.50 on Steam Days)
Family Tickets £21.50 (£25.50 Steam Days)
Senior Citizens £6.50 (£7.50 Steam Days)
Note: Special event tickets should be pre-booked.

Detailed Directions by Car:
From All Parts: Exit the M4 at Junction 18. Follow the A46 towards Bath and at the junction with the A420 turn right towards Bristol. At Bridge Yate turn left onto the A4175 and continue until you reach the A431. Turn right and Bitton Station is 100 yards on the right.

BARROW HILL ROUNDHOUSE RAILWAY CENTRE

Address: Barrow Hill Roundhouse, Campbell Drive, Barrow Hill, Staveley, Chesterfield   S43 2PR
Telephone Nº: (01246) 472450
Year Formed: 1998
Location: Staveley, near Chesterfield
Length of Line: ¾ mile

Nº of Steam Locos: 12
Nº of Other Locos: Over 40
Nº of Members: Approximately 400
Annual Membership Fee: £22.00 (Adult)
Approx Nº of Visitors P.A.: 30,000
Gauge: Standard
Web site: www.barrowhill.org

GENERAL INFORMATION

Nearest Mainline Station: Chesterfield (3½ miles)
Nearest Bus Station: Chesterfield (3 miles)
Car Parking: Space available for 300 cars
Coach Parking: Available
Souvenir Shop(s): Yes
Food & Drinks: Yes – Café

SPECIAL INFORMATION

Britain's last remaining operational railway roundhouse provides storage and repair facilities for standard gauge steam, diesel and electric locomotives. In Autumn 2017, renovations were completed which added a museum and a café.

OPERATING INFORMATION

Opening Times: Every weekend from 2nd March 2019 until 15th December 2019. Please check the centre's web site for updates and details of special events.
Steam Working: See above.
Prices: Adults £3.00
Children £2.00
Family Tickets £8.00 (2 adults + 3 children)

Detailed Directions by Car:
Exit the M1 at Junction 30 and take the A619 to Staveley (about 3½ miles). Pass through Staveley, turn right at Troughbrook Road. Continue along for ½ mile, pass under the railway bridge and take the turn immediately on the right. Turn left onto Campbell Drive and the Roundhouse is on the left. The railway is signposted with Brown Tourist signs.

THE BATTLEFIELD LINE

Address: The Battlefield Line, Shackerstone Station, Shackerstone, Leicestershire   CV13 6NW
Telephone Nº: (01827) 880754
Year Formed: 1968
Location of Line: The line runs through Market Bosworth
Length of Line: 5 miles

Nº of Steam Locos: 5
Nº of Other Locos: 20
Nº of Members: 500 approximately
Annual Membership Fee: £18.00 Adult; £50.00 Family
Approx Nº of Visitors P.A.: 60,000
Gauge: Standard
Web site: www.battlefieldline.co.uk

GENERAL INFORMATION

Nearest Mainline Station: Nuneaton or Hinckley (both 12 miles)
Nearest Bus Station: Hinckley (for Market Bosworth)
Car Parking: Ample free parking available
Coach Parking: At Market Bosworth Station
Souvenir Shop(s): At Shackerstone Station
Food & Drinks: Yes – Buffets available at all stations

SPECIAL INFORMATION

Travel from the Grade II listed Shackerstone Station through the beautiful Leicestershire countryside with views of the adjoining Ashby Canal. Arrive at the award-winning Shenton Station and explore Bosworth Battlefield (1485) before making the return journey.

OPERATING INFORMATION

Operating Info: 2019 dates: Weekends and Bank Holidays from 30th March to 10th November. Santa Specials operate on weekends from 1st December to Christmas Eve. Also open from Tuesday to Thursday in July and August, on Wednesdays in June, September & October and from 28th December 2019 to 1st January 2020.
Please check the web site for further details.
Opening Times: 11.00am to 4.15pm
Steam Working: From 11.15am to 4.15pm during high season and 11.00am to 3.30pm at other times.
Prices: Adult Return £12.00   O.A.P. Return £9.00
        Child Return £6.00 (ages 5-15 years)
        Family Ticket £30.00
                (2 adults and 3 children)

Detailed Directions by Car:
Follow the brown tourist signs from the A444 or A447 heading towards the market town of Market Bosworth. Continue towards the villages of Congerstone & Shackerstone and finally to Shackerstone Station. Access is only available via the Old Trackbed.

BEAMISH,
THE LIVING MUSEUM OF THE NORTH

Address: Beamish, The Living Museum of the North, Beamish DH9 0RG	**Nº of Steam Locos**: 15
Telephone Nº: (0191) 370-4000	**Nº of Other Locos**: 2
	N.B.: Not all Locos are on display
Year Formed: 1970	**Approx Nº of Visitors P.A.**: 765,000
Length of Line: ½ mile	**Web site**: www.beamish.org.uk

GENERAL INFORMATION

Nearest Mainline Station: Newcastle Central (8 miles); Durham City (12 miles)
Nearest Bus Station: Newcastle (8 miles); Durham (12 miles)
Car Parking: Free parking for 2,000 cars
Coach Parking: Free parking for 40 coaches
Souvenir Shop(s): Yes
Food & Drinks: Yes – self service tea room, licensed period Public House, Coffee shop and a coal-fired Fish & Chip shop!

SPECIAL INFORMATION

A replica of William Hedley's famous 1813 locomotive "Puffing Billy" steams on the Pockerley Waggonway at Beamish alongside replicas of Locomotion and the Steam Elephant.

OPERATING INFORMATION

Opening Times: Open all year round: from 10.00am to 4.00pm in the Winter (November to March). Closed on Mondays and Fridays in the Winter. Open from 10.00am to 5.00pm during the Summer (April to October). Check for Christmas opening times.
Allow 4-5 hours for a Summer visit and three hours in the Winter.
Steam Working: Daily during the Summer
Prices: Adult £19.50
        Child £11.50
        Senior Citizen £14.50
Children under 5 are admitted free.
Special Family Tickets are available.
Tickets allow unlimited free return visits for 12 months from the date of first visit but are not valid for the Evening events.

Detailed Directions by Car:
From North & South: Follow the A1(M) to Junction 63 (Chester-le-street) and then take A693 for 4 miles towards Stanley; From North-West: Take the A68 south to Castleside near Consett and follow the signs on the A692 and A693 via Stanley.

THE BLUEBELL RAILWAY

Address: The Bluebell Railway, Sheffield Park Station, near Uckfield   TN22 3QL
Telephone Nº: (01825) 720800
Year Formed: 1959
Location: Near Uckfield, East Sussex
Length of Line: 11 miles
Web site: www.bluebell-railway.co.uk

Nº of Steam Locos: Over 30 with up to 3 in operation on any given day
Nº of Other Locos: −
Nº of Members: 10,000 (approximately)
Annual Membership Fee: £25.00 Adult
Approx Nº of Visitors P.A.: 140,000
Gauge: Standard

GENERAL INFORMATION

Nearest Mainline Station: East Grinstead (2 minute walk)
Nearest Bus Station: East Grinstead
Car Parking: Parking is available at Sheffield Park and Horsted Keynes Stations.
Coach Parking: Sheffield Park is best for coaches
Souvenir Shop(s): Yes – at Sheffield Park Station
Food & Drinks: Yes – buffets and licensed bars & restaurant

SPECIAL INFORMATION

The Railway runs 'Golden Arrow' dining trains on most Saturday evenings and Sunday lunchtimes. There is also a museum at Sheffield Park Station.

OPERATING INFORMATION

Opening Times: 2019 dates: Open every weekend and Bank Holiday from 16th February to 3rd November inclusive. Also open Wednesday to Fridayfrom April to 1st November and daily from 22nd May to 8th September. Please contact the railway for further information. Santa Specials operate on weekends and other dates in December. Open from approximately 10.30am to 5.30pm
Steam Working: As above
Prices: Adult Return £19.00
             Child Return £9.50
             Family Return £49.00 (2 adult + 3 child)
                       and £34.00 (1 adult + 3 child)
Note: Prices are cheaper if purchased at least 8 days in advance of a visit.

Detailed Directions by Car:
Sheffield Park Station is situated on the A275 Wych Cross to Lewes road. Horsted Keynes Station is signposted from the B2028 Lingfield to Haywards Heath road.

BODMIN & WENFORD RAILWAY

Address: Bodmin General Station, Losthwithiel Road, Bodmin, Cornwall PL31 1AQ	**Nº of Steam Locos:** 11
	Nº of Other Locos: 9
	Nº of Members: 1,200
Telephone Nº: (01208) 73555	**Annual Membership Fee:** £18.00
Year Formed: 1984	**Approx Nº of Visitors P.A.:** 62,000
Location of Line: Bodmin Parkway to Boscarne Junction, via Bodmin General	**Gauge:** Standard
	Web site: www.bodminrailway.co.uk
Length of Line: 6½ miles	**E-mail:** enquiries@bodminrailway.co.uk

GENERAL INFORMATION

Nearest Mainline Station: Bodmin Parkway (cross platform interchange with the Bodmin & Wenford Railway)
Car Parking: Free parking at Bodmin General
Coach Parking: Free parking at Bodmin General
Souvenir Shop(s): Yes
Food & Drinks: Yes

SPECIAL INFORMATION

The Railway has steep gradients and through tickets to "Bodmin & Wenford Railway" are available from all Mainline stations.

OPERATING INFORMATION

Opening Times: 2019 dates: Daily from 14th May to 29th September. Also during various other dates in February, March, April and October (including most weekends). Santa Specials run on December weekends and with other specials operating 31st December 2019 to 2nd January 2020. Open 10.00am to 5.00pm on most days. Please contact the railway for further details.
Steam Working: Most trains are steam-hauled except for some Saturdays when Heritage diesels are used. Daily steam throughout August.
Prices: Adult All Day Rover £13.50
Senior Citizen All Day Rover £12.50
Child All Day Rover £6.50 (Under-3s free)
Family Day Rover £36.00 (2 adult + 4 child)

Detailed Directions by Car:
From the A30/A38/A389 follow the signs to Bodmin Town Centre then follow the brown tourist signs showing the steam engine logo to the Steam Railway on the B3268 Losthwithiel Road.

BO'NESS & KINNEIL RAILWAY

Address: Bo'ness Station, Union Street, Bo'ness, West Lothian EH51 9AQ	**Nº of Steam Locos:** 26 **Other Locos:** 25
Telephone Nº: (01506) 822298	**Nº of Members:** 1,500
Year Opened: 1981	**Annual Membership Fee:** £22.00
Location of Line: Bo'ness to Manuel	**Approx Nº of Visitors P.A.:** 70,000
Length of Line: 5 miles	**Gauge:** Standard
	Web site: www.bkrailway.co.uk

Photo courtesy of Peter Backhouse

GENERAL INFORMATION

Nearest Mainline Station: Linlithgow (3 miles)
Nearest Bus Station: Bo'ness (¼ mile)
Car Parking: Free parking at Bo'ness Station
Coach Parking: Free parking at Bo'ness Station
Souvenir Shop(s): Yes
Food & Drinks: Yes

SPECIAL INFORMATION

In addition to the ten-mile journey, passengers should visit Scotland's largest railway museum at Bo'ness Station. The Railway and Museum are operated by volunteers from The Scottish Railway Preservation Society.

OPERATING INFORMATION

Opening Times: 2019 dates: Weekends from 23rd March to 3rd November inclusive. Also open for mid-week running on selected dates and most days in July and August. Santa Specials operate on weekends in December and Hogmanay Black Bun Trains run from 29th – 31st December. The museum is open daily from 23rd March to 27th October.
Steam Working: On standard service days, 10.45am, 12.10pm and 2.10pm. The 3.35pm service may be diesel-hauled at weekends.
Prices: Adult Day Ticket £10.00   Child Day £6.00
Family Day Ticket £28.00   Concession Day £9.00
Note: Group discounts are available. Under-5s free. Special fares may apply on Special Event Days.

Detailed Directions by Car:
From Edinburgh: Take the M9 and exit at Junction 3. Then take the A904 to Bo'ness; From Glasgow: Take the M80 to M876 and then M9 (South). Exit at Junction 5 and take A904 to Bo'ness; From the North: Take M9 (South), exit at Junction 5, then take A904 to Bo'ness; From Fife: Leave the A90 after the Forth Bridge, then take A904 to Bo'ness.

BOWES RAILWAY AND MUSEUM

Address: Bowes Railway, Springwell Road, Gateshead, Tyne & Wear NE9 7QJ	**No of Steam Locos**: 2
Telephone No: (0191) 416-1847	**No of Other Locos**: 5
Year Formed: 1976	**Approx No of Visitors P.A.**: 5,000
Location of Line: Springwell Village	**Gauge**: Standard
Length of Line: 1¼ miles	**Web site**: www.bowesrailway.uk

GENERAL INFORMATION

Nearest Mainline Station: Newcastle Central (3 miles)
Nearest Bus Station: Gateshead Interchange (2 miles)
Car Parking: Free parking at site
Coach Parking: Free parking at site
Souvenir Shop(s): Open Thursday to Saturday throughout the year
Food & Drinks: Available

SPECIAL INFORMATION

Designed by George Stephenson and opened in 1826, the Railway is a scheduled Ancient Monument which operated unique preserved standard gauge rope-hauled inclines and steam hauled passenger trains.

OPERATING INFORMATION

Opening Times: The Springwell site is open for static viewing on Thursdays, Fridays, Saturdays and Sundays throughout the year – 10.00am to 3.00pm.
Steam Working: None at present
Prices: Adults £2.00 (Over-16s)
　　　　　Children £1.00
　　　　　Adult Season Ticket £5.00
　　　　　Child Season Ticket £3.00

Detailed Directions by Car:
From A1 (Northbound): Follow the A194(M) to the Tyne Tunnel and turn left at the sign for Springwell.
From A1 (Southbound): Take the turn off left for the B1288 to Springwell and Wrekenton.

BRESSINGHAM STEAM MUSEUM

Address: Bressingham Steam Museum, Bressingham, Diss, Norfolk IP22 2AB
Telephone Nº: (01379) 686900
Year Formed: Mid 1950's
Location of Line: Bressingham, Near Diss
Length of Line: 5 miles in total (4 lines)

Nº of Steam Locos: 6 Standard gauge plus many others
Approx Nº of Visitors P.A.: 80,000+
Gauge: Standard, 2 foot, 10¼ inches and 15 inches
Web site: www.bressingham.co.uk

GENERAL INFORMATION

Nearest Mainline Station: Diss (2½ miles)
Nearest Bus Station: Bressingham (1¼ miles)
Car Parking: Free parking for 400 cars available
Coach Parking: Free parking for 5 coaches
Souvenir Shop(s): Yes
Food & Drinks: Yes

SPECIAL INFORMATION

In addition to Steam locomotives, Bressingham has a large selection of steam traction engines, fixed steam engines and also the National Dad's Army Museum, two extensive gardens and a water garden centre.

OPERATING INFORMATION

Opening Times: 2019 dates: Daily from 29th March to 27th October. Open from 10.30am to 5.00pm.
Steam Working: Almost every operating day except for most (but not all) Mondays and Tuesdays in April, May, June, July, September and October. Please contact the Museum for further details.
Prices: Adult £12.49 (non-Steam) £15.49 (Steam)
Child £7.99 (non-Steam) £9.99 (Steam)
Seniors £11.49 (non-Steam) £14.49 (Steam)
Note: Reduced entry charges are available for visitors who do not take railway rides. The prices shown include an optional donation of 10%.

Detailed Directions by Car:
From All Parts: Take the A11 to Thetford and then follow the A1066 towards Diss for Bressingham. The Museum is signposted by the brown tourist signs. SATNAV please use the following post code: IP22 2AA

BRISTOL HARBOUR RAILWAY

Address: Princes Wharf, Wapping Road, Bristol BS1 4RN **Telephone N°:** (0117) 352-6600 **Year Formed:** 1978 **Location of Line:** South side of the Floating Harbour	**Length of Line:** Just under 1 mile **N° of Steam Locos:** 2 **N° of Other Locos:** 1 **Gauge:** Standard **Web site:** mshed.org

GENERAL INFORMATION

Nearest Mainline Station: Bristol Temple Meads (1 mile)
Nearest Bus Station: City Centre (½ mile)
Car Parking: Pay & Display adjacent to M Shed
Coach Parking: Pay & Display adjacent
Souvenir Shop(s): In the M Shed Museum
Food & Drinks: Café in the Museum

SPECIAL INFORMATION

The M Shed museum opened in June 2011 and has since attracted over 1 million visitors. Trains run alongside the harbour to link M Shed with the SS Great Britain on the dockside and from M Shed to Ashton Bridge along the New Cut, giving a choice of scenery on alternate routes.

OPERATING INFORMATION

Opening Times: 2019 dates: 16th, 17th, 30th & 31st March; 13th, 14th, 20th & 22nd April; 4th to 6th and 25th to 27th May; 8th, 9th, 15th, 16th 29th & 30th June. Trains run from 11.00am to 4.00pm.
Steam Working: Every operating day.
Prices: Singles £2.50
　　　　　M Shed to Vauxhall Bridge Return £3.50
Note: Children under the age of 6 travel for free.

Detailed Directions by Car:
From All Parts: Follow signs to Bristol City Centre and then the Brown Tourist signs for the Museum. A good landmark to look out for are the 4 huge quayside cranes.

BUCKINGHAMSHIRE RAILWAY CENTRE

Address: Quainton Road Station, Quainton, Aylesbury, Bucks. HP22 4BY **Telephone N°:** (01296) 655720 **Year Formed:** 1969 **Location of Line:** At Quainton on the old Metropolitan/Great Central Line **Length of Line:** 2 × ½ mile demo tracks	**N° of Steam Locos:** 30 **N° of Other Locos:** 6 **N° of Members:** 1,000 **Annual Membership Fee:** £25.00 **Approx N° of Visitors P.A.:** 35,000 **Gauge:** Standard (also a Miniature line) **Recorded Info. Line:** (01296) 655450

GENERAL INFORMATION

Nearest Mainline Station: Aylesbury (6 miles)
Nearest Bus Station: Aylesbury
Car Parking: Free parking for 500 cars available
Coach Parking: Free parking for 10 coaches
Souvenir Shop(s): Yes
Food & Drinks: Yes

SPECIAL INFORMATION

In addition to a large collection of locomotives and carriages, the Centre has an extensive ½ mile outdoor miniature railway system operated by the Vale of Aylesbury Model Engineering Society.

Web site: www.bucksrailcentre.org
E-mail: office@bucksrailcentre.org

OPERATING INFORMATION

Opening Times: 2019 dates: Monday to Wednesday for static viewing only from 1st April to 30th September. Trains run on Sundays and Bank Holidays between these dates and on Wednesdays during the school holidays. There are also other Special Event days. Contact the railway for details.
Steam Working: All operating days.
Prices: Adult £6.00, £12.00 and £14.00
　　　　Child £4.00, £8.00 and £10.00
　　　　　　(Under 5's travel free of charge)
　　　　Senior Citizen £5.00, £11.00 and £13.00
　　　　Family £17.00, £34.50 and £42.50
　　　　　　(2 adults + up to 4 children)
Note: Prices shown above are for static viewing, Steam Days and Special Event days respectively. 'Thomas' Days are more expensive still.

Detailed Directions by Car:
The Buckinghamshire Railway Centre is signposted off the A41 Aylesbury to Bicester Road at Waddesdon and off the A413 Buckingham to Aylesbury road at Whitchurch. Junctions 7, 8 and 9 of the M40 are all close by.

CALEDONIAN RAILWAY

Address: The Station, Park Road, Brechin, Angus DD9 7AF	**N° of Steam Locos**: 5 **Other Locos**: 10
Telephone N°: (01356) 622992 (Available on operating days only)	**N° of Members**: 250
Year Formed: 1979	**Annual Membership Fee**: Adult £15.00; Family £25.00; Senior £12.00; Junior £6
Location: Brechin to the Bridge of Dun	**Approx N° of Visitors P.A.**: 12,000
Length of Line: 4 miles	**Gauge**: Standard
	Web site: www.caledonianrailway.com

GENERAL INFORMATION

Nearest Mainline Station: Montrose (4½ miles)
Nearest Bus Station: Brechin (200 yards)
Car Parking: Ample free parking at both Stations
Coach Parking: Free parking at both Stations
Souvenir Shop(s): Yes
Food & Drinks: Light refreshments are available

SPECIAL INFORMATION

Brechin Station is the only original Terminus station in preservation.

OPERATING INFORMATION

Opening Times: 2019 dates: Easter Sundays, Santa Specials operate on some December weekends. Also open every weekend from 20th April to 8th September and for some other Special Events throughout the year. Please check the web site for further details.
Trains usually run from 11.00am to 3.00pm.
Steam Working: Steam service on every operating Sunday in addition to other Special Events days.
Prices: Adult Return £8.00
         Child Return £6.00   (Under-3s free)
         Senior Citizen Return £7.00
         Family Return £25.00 (2 Adult + 3 Child)
Higher fares may apply for Special Event days and All Day tickets are also available.

Detailed Directions by Car:
From South: For Brechin Station, leave the A90 at the Brechin turn-off and go straight through the Town Centre. Pass the Northern Hotel, take the 2nd exit at the mini-roundabout then it is 150 yards to Park Road/St. Ninian Square; From North: For Brechin Station, leave the A90 at the Brechin turn-off and go straight through Trinity Village. Turn left at the mini-roundabout, it is then 250 yards to Park Road/St. Ninian Square. Bridge of Dun is situated half way between Brechin and Montrose. (Follow tourist signs).

CAMBRIAN HERITAGE RAILWAYS

Address: Old Station Building, Oswald Road, Oswestry SY11 4RE	**N⁰ of Steam Locos**: 4 (under repair)
Telephone N⁰: (01691) 728131	**N⁰ of Other Locos**: 2 DMUs + 7 others
Year Formed: 2009	**N⁰ of Members**: 500+
Location of Line: Llynclys and Oswestry	**Annual Membership Fee**: £18.00 (Adult)
Length of Line: Almost 1 mile at each site	**Approx N⁰ of Visitors P.A.**: 15,000
	Gauge: Standard
	Web site: www.cambrianrailways.com

GENERAL INFORMATION

Nearest Mainline Station: Gobowen (3 miles from Oswestry – 7 miles from Llynclys)
Nearest Bus Station: Oswestry
Car Parking: Available at both sites
Coach Parking: Please contact the railway's Coach Tour officer for further information.
Souvenir Shop(s): Yes
Food & Drinks: Available

SPECIAL INFORMATION

Cambrian Heritage Railways currently operate at two separate sites along the 8½ mile Gobowen to Llanyblodwel line. The short to medium term aim is to link the two sites to make a 6 mile long heritage railway and the CHR is currently extending the operational line at Oswestry towards Llynclys.

OPERATING INFORMATION

Opening Times: 2019 dates: Open every Saturday, Sunday and Bank Holiday from April to September and also on some other dates. Santa Specials run on some Saturdays in December. Check the web site for further details.
Trains run from 11.00am to 4.00pm at Llynclys and until 3.00pm at Oswestry.
Steam Working: Hired steam locos operate at peak times. Please check the website for further details.
Prices: Adults £5.00 or £8.00 (Joint ticket)
  Concessions £4.00 or £6.00 (Joint ticket)
  Children £3.00 or £5.00 (Joint ticket)
  Family £12.00 or £20.00 (2 adult + 2 child)
Note: Prices shown are for "Full Day Rover" tickets on Diesel-hauled days. Higher fares may apply on Steam-hauled days. Joint tickets cover both locations

---

Detailed Directions by Car:
The Llynclys site is situated on the B4396 approximately 5 miles southwest of Oswestry, just off the A483 heading towards Welshpool. Turn left at Llyncly Crossroads towards Knockin. The entrance to the site is on the right after about 400 yards, immediately over the railway bridge. The Oswestry site is near the town centre and is clearly signposted.

CHASEWATER RAILWAY (THE COLLIERY LINE)

Address: Chasewater Country Park, Pool Lane, Burntwood   WS8 7NL
Telephone Nº: (01543) 452623
Year Re-formed: 1985
Location: Chasewater Country Park, near Brownhills, Walsall
Length of Line: 2 miles

Nº of Steam Locos: 12 (4 in service)
Nº of Other Locos: 15 (3 in service)
Approx Nº of Visitors P.A.: 45,000
Gauge: Standard
Web site: www.chasewaterrailway.co.uk

GENERAL INFORMATION

Nearest Mainline Station: Walsall or Cannock (both approximately 8 miles)
Nearest Bus Station: Lichfield (8½ miles)
Car Parking: Free parking in Chasewater Park
Coach Parking: Free parking in Chasewater Park
Souvenir Shop(s): Yes
Food & Drinks: Yes

SPECIAL INFORMATION

Chasewater Railway is based on the Cannock Chase & Wolverhampton Railway opened in 1856. The railway passed into the hands of the National Coal Board which ceased using the line in 1965. Trains operate between Brownhills West and Chasetown.

OPERATING INFORMATION

Opening Times: 2019 dates: Weekends and Bank Holiday Mondays from April to September plus Sundays in October and November. Also open on some Tuesdays and/or Thursdays during the school holidays and for Halloween, Santa Specials and other events. Please check the web site for further information. A regular service runs from 11.00am on operating days.
Steam Working: Please check the web site or phone the railway for further details.
Prices: Adult Day Rover £6.50
Child Day Rover £4.50 (Under-3s free)
Concession Day Rover £5.50
Family Day Rover £19.50
All tickets offer unlimited rides on the day of issue.

Detailed Directions by Car:
Chasewater Country Park is situated in Brownhills off the A5 southbound near the junction of the A5 with the A452 Chester Road. Follow the Brown tourist signs on the A5 for the Country Park.

CHATHAM HISTORIC DOCKYARD RAILWAY

Address: Dock Road, Chatham
Telephone Nº: (01634) 823800
Year Formed: 2001
Location of Line: Chatham, Kent
Length of Line: ¾ mile

Nº of Steam Locos: 5
Nº of Other Locos: 3
Gauge: Standard and also 18 inches
Web site: thedockyard.co.uk (no www.)
Contact Address: N.K.I.L.S.,
69 West Street, Gillingham   ME7 1EF

GENERAL INFORMATION

Nearest Mainline Station: Chatham (1½ miles)
Nearest Bus Station: Gillingham (1½ miles)
Car Parking: Available on site
Coach Parking: Available
Souvenir Shop(s): Yes
Food & Drinks: Available

SPECIAL INFORMATION

The Dockyard Railway is operated by North Kent Industrial Locomotive Society and runs demonstrations of freight steaming at Chatham's Historic Dockyard (www.chdt.org.uk). Almost one mile of line is available for these demonstrations but train rides are not available.

OPERATING INFORMATION

Opening Times: 2019 dates: 2nd February to 24th November. Open from 10.00am but closing time varies depending on the time of the year.
Steam Working: Please contact the Dockyard for further information. Please note that the Railway does not offer train rides.
Prices: Adults £25.00
        Children (Aged 5-15 years old) £15.00
        Concessions £22.50
        Family Tickets £66.00
Note: Prices shown are for admission to the Dockyard. Tickets are valid for 12 months. Entrance to some special events is an additional charge.

Detailed Directions by Car:
From All Parts: Exit the M2 at Junction 3 and follow the A229 to Chatham. Follow the Brown tourist signs which clearly mark the correct route to the Dockyard.

CHINNOR & PRINCES RISBOROUGH RAILWAY

Address: Station Road, Chinnor, Oxon, OX39 4ER	**Nº of Steam Locos:** 1
	Nº of Other Locos: 6
Telephone Nº: 07979 055366	**Nº of Members:** 850
Year Formed: 1989	**Annual Membership Fee:** Adult £25.00;
Location: Chinnor to Princes Risborough	Family £40.00; Child £10.00; OAP £20.00
Length of Line: 4 miles	**Approx Nº of Visitors P.A.:** 15,000
Gauge: Standard	**Web Site:** www.chinnorrailway.co.uk

GENERAL INFORMATION

Nearest Mainline Station: Princes Risborough Interchange allows direct access to Mainline trains.
Nearest Bus Station: High Wycombe (10 miles)
Car Parking: Free parking available at Chinnor
Coach Parking: Prior arrangement preferred but not necessary
Souvenir Shop(s): Yes
Food & Drinks: Soft drinks and light snacks in Station Buffet. Buffet usually available on trains.

SPECIAL INFORMATION

The Chinnor & Princes Risborough Railway operates the remaining 4 mile section of the former GWR Watlington Branch from Chinnor to Thame Junction and links with national rail services at Princes Risborough.

OPERATING INFORMATION

Opening Times: 2019 dates: Sundays and Bank Holiday Mondays from 31st March to 27th October and also Santa Specials on weekends in December. Please check the railway's website for details of other bookable special and evening events during the year.
Steam Working: Operates from 11.00am to 4.30pm on Sundays and Bank Holidays
Prices: Adult Return £12.00   Child Return £3.00
Family Return £30.00 (2 adult + 2 child)
Senior Citizen Return £10.00
Note: Discounts are available for advance purchases

Detailed Directions by Car:
From All Parts: The railway at Chinnor is situated in Station Road just off the B4009. Junction 6 of the M40 is 4 miles away and Princes Risborough 4 miles further along the B4009. Once in Chinnor follow the brown Tourist signs to the railway.

CHOLSEY & WALLINGFORD RAILWAY

Address: Wallingford Station, 5 Hithercroft Road, Wallingford, Oxon, OX10 9GQ	**N° of Steam Locos**: Visiting locos only
	N° of Other Locos: 5
	N° of Members: 250
Telephone N°: (01491) 835067 (24hr info)	**Annual Membership Fee**: £20.00
Year Formed: 1981	**Approx N° of Visitors P.A.**: 9,700
Location of Line: Wallingford, Oxon.	**Gauge**: Standard
Length of Line: 2½ miles	**Web**: www.cholsey-wallingford-railway.com

GENERAL INFORMATION

Nearest Mainline Station: Joint station at Cholsey
Nearest Bus Station: Wallingford (¼ mile)
Car Parking: Off road parking available
Coach Parking: Off road parking available
Souvenir Shop(s): Yes
Food & Drinks: Yes

SPECIAL INFORMATION

The Wallingford branch (now known as "The Bunk Line") was originally intended as a through line to Princes Risborough, via Watlington, but became the first standard gauge branch of Brunel's broad-gauge London to Bristol line.

OPERATING INFORMATION

Opening Times: Selected weekends from Easter until Christmas with trains running from 11.00am to 4.00pm – please phone the railway or check the web site for further details.
Steam Working: The railway will have visiting steam locomotives from time to time. Please contact the railway for further information.
Prices: Adult Return £10.00
Child Return £7.00 (Under-5s free)
Concessionary Return £8.00
Family Return £24.00 (2 adult + 2 child)
Prices: Prices may be subject to change for Engine visits and other special events.

Detailed Directions by Car:
From All Parts: Exit from the A34 at the Milton Interchange (between E. Ilsley and Abingdon). Follow signs to Didcot and Wallingford (A4130). Take Wallingford bypass, then turn left at the first roundabout (signposted Hithercroft Road). The Station is then ½ mile on the right.

CHURNET VALLEY RAILWAY

Address: Kingsley & Froghall Station, Froghall, Stoke-on-Trent ST10 2HA	**Nº of Steam Locos:** 6 (2 in operation)
Telephone Nº: (01538) 750755	**Nº of Other Locos:** 11 (3 in operation)
Year Formed: 1978	**Approx Nº of Visitors P.A.:** 70,000
Location of Line: Kingsley & Froghall to Cheddleton	**Gauge:** Standard
	Web: www.churnet-valley-railway.co.uk

Length: 5¼ miles (plus a further 8 miles when operating on the Cauldon Branch)

Photo courtesy of D.R. Gibson

GENERAL INFORMATION

Nearest Mainline Station: Stoke-on-Trent (12 miles)
Nearest Bus Station: Leek (5 miles)
Car Parking: Parking available on site
Coach Parking: Restricted space available at Kingsley & Froghall Station.
Souvenir Shop(s): Yes
Food & Drinks: Yes

SPECIAL INFORMATION

Cheddleton Station is a Grade II listed building, Consall is a sleepy halt with Victorian charm, whereas Kingsley & Froghall has been rebuilt in NSR style and includes disabled facilities and a tearoom.

OPERATING INFORMATION

Opening Times: 2019 dates: Most Sundays from 3rd February until 20th October; most Saturdays from April to September inclusive; Every Wednesday from end May to the end of September and all Bank Holiday Mondays plus a number of other Special Event days. Please check the web site or contact the railway for timetable details and any other information.
Steam Working: Most operating days except for Diesel Gala days.
Prices: Adult Day Rover £12.00
Child Day Rover £6.00
Senior Citizen Day Rover £10.00
Family Ticket Day Rover £30.00
Note: Fare for special event days are much higher.

Detailed Directions by Car:
From All Parts: Take the M6 to Stoke-on-Trent and follow roads to Ashbourne or Leek. Cheddleton Station is off the A520 Leek to Stone road (SatNav ST13 7EE). Kingsley & Froghall Station is off the A52 Ashbourne Road.

COLEFORD GWR MUSEUM

Address: The Old Railway Station, Railway Drive, Coleford GL16 8RH	**N° of Steam Locos:** 1
Telephone N°: (01594) 833569	**N° of Other Locos:** 2 (7¼ inches)
Year Formed: 1988	**Approx N° of Visitors P.A.:** Not known
Location of Line: Coleford	**Gauge:** 7¼ inches and Standard gauge
Length of Line: 100 yards	**Website:** www.gwrmuseumcoleford.co.uk

GENERAL INFORMATION

Nearest Mainline Station: Lydney (7½ miles)
Nearest Bus Station: Gloucester (20 miles)
Car Parking: Low cost parking available on site
Coach Parking: Not available
Souvenir Shop(s): No souvenirs but a number of railway books are available for purchase.
Food & Drinks: Tea and Coffee available only

SPECIAL INFORMATION

Based in the 1883 Goods Shed at Coleford, the Museum chronicles the history of railways in the Forest of Dean.

OPERATING INFORMATION

Opening Times: 2019 dates: Friday and Saturday afternoons and Bank Holidays throughout the year. Open from 2.30pm to 5.00pm.
Steam Working: The standard gauge loco is not currently in service but steam rides are available via the two 7¼ inch locos.
Prices: Adults £4.00 (admission to the museum)
Children £2.00 (admission to the museum)
Miniature Railway Rides £2.00
Peckett Footplate Visit £2.00 (if steaming)

Detailed Directions by Car:
From All Parts: From the M50 take the A40 at Ross-on-Wye to Monmouth then the A4136 towards Cinderford. Turn off the A4136 into Coleford and the Museum is located in the Town Centre.

COLNE VALLEY RAILWAY

Address: Castle Hedingham Station, Yeldham Road, Castle Hedingham, Essex, CO9 3DZ **Telephone Nº**: (01787) 461174 **Year Formed**: 1974 **Location**: 7 miles north-west of Braintree **Length of Line**: Approximately 1 mile	**Nº of Steam Locos**: 7 **Nº of Other Locos**: 11 **Approx Nº of Visitors P.A.**: 45,000 **Gauge**: Standard and 7¼ inches **Web Site**: www.colnevalleyrailway.co.uk

GENERAL INFORMATION

Nearest Mainline Station: Braintree (7 miles)
Nearest Bus Station: Hedingham bus from Braintree stops at the Railway (except on Sundays)
Car Parking: Parking at the site
Coach Parking: Free parking at site
Souvenir Shop(s): Yes
Food & Drinks: Yes – on operational days. Also Pullman Sunday Lunches – bookings necessary.

SPECIAL INFORMATION

The railway has been re-built on a section of the old Colne Valley & Halstead Railway, with all buildings, bridges, signal boxes, etc. re-located on site.

OPERATING INFORMATION

Opening Times: 2019 dates: Steam trains run every Sunday and Bank Holiday weekend from 24th March to 27th October plus Wednesdays during the School Holidays. Diesel trains run on every Saturday from 23rd March to 2nd November. Pre-booked parties by arrangement and various other special events. Check the web site for details.
Steam Working: Site opens at 10.30am. Trains run from 11.30am. Last admission at 3.00pm.
Prices: Adult – Steam days £10.00; Diesel £8.00
Child – Steam £5.00; Diesel £4.00
Family (2 adults + 2 children) –
Steam £27.50; Diesel £22.00
Senior Citizen – Steam £7.50; Diesel £6.00

Detailed Directions by Car:
Exit the M11 at Junction 8 (Stanstead Airport) and follow the A120 eastwards to Braintree. Take the A131 northwards to High Garrett and bear left at the traffic lights onto the A1017 signposted Haverhill. Follow this road for 6 miles and the entrance to the railway is on the right past the villages of Gosfield and Sible Hedingham.

CREWE HERITAGE CENTRE

Address: Vernon Way, Crewe, CW1 2DB	**Nº of Steam Locos**: 1
Telephone Nº: (01270) 212130	**Nº of Other Locos**: 3
Year Formed: 1987	**Approx Nº of Visitors P.A.**: 15,000
Location of Line: Crewe Heritage Centre	**Gauge**: 7¼ inches and Standard Gauge
Length of Line: 300 yards (Standard gauge) and 600 yards (7¼ inch gauge)	**Web site**: www.crewehc.org

GENERAL INFORMATION

Nearest Mainline Station: Crewe (¾ mile)
Nearest Bus Station: Crewe (½ mile)
Car Parking: Available on site
Coach Parking: None
Souvenir Shop(s): Yes
Food & Drinks: Tea and Coffee only

SPECIAL INFORMATION

Crewe Heritage Centre is an operational base for numerous mainline steam charters with various locomotives present throughout the year.

OPERATING INFORMATION

Opening Times: Weekends and Bank Holidays from April until the end of October. Open 10.00am to 4.30pm with last admissions at 3.30pm.
Steam Working: Please contact the Centre for details.
Prices: Adults £6.00
Children £4.00
Concessions £4.00
Family Tickets £14.00

Detailed Directions by Car:
From All Parts: Exit the M6 at Junction 16 and take the A500 into Crewe. Follow the brown tourist signs for "The Railway Age". The Heritage Centre is adjacent to Crewe Railway Station and next to the Tesco Supermarket.

THE DARTMOOR RAILWAY

Address: Okehampton Station, Station Road, Okehampton EX20 1EJ	**Length of Line**: 15½ miles (Heritage service operates on 3½ miles of the line)
Telephone Nº: (01837) 52762	**Nº of Steam Locos**: Visiting locos only
Year Formed: 1997	**Nº of Other Locos**: 2 and DMUs
Location of Line: Meldon to Okehampton	**Gauge**: Standard
	Web site: www.dartmoorrailway.com

GENERAL INFORMATION

Nearest Mainline Station: Crediton
Nearest Bus Station: Okehampton
Car Parking: Okehampton Station and some spaces at Sampford Courtenay Station – all free of charge
Coach Parking: Okehampton Station
Souvenir Shop(s): Yes
Food & Drinks: Okehampton Buffet and Meldon Buffet are open on Bank Holidays and other operating days. The Buffets are fully licensed.

SPECIAL INFORMATION

The railway operates on the route of the old Southern Railway line through the mid-Devon countryside to the northern slopes of Dartmoor National Park.

OPERATING INFORMATION

Opening Times: 2019 heritage services will operate on weekends and Bank Holidays from Good Friday until September, departing Okehampton hourly from 10.15am to 4.35pm.
Steam Working: Please contact the railway for further information.
Prices: Adult £5.00 (Day rover ticket)
Concession £4.00 (Day rover ticket)
Child (ages 5 to 15) £3.00 (Day rover ticket)
Under-5s travel free of charge
Family Ticket £14.00 (2 adult + 2 children)

Detailed Directions by Car:
From All Parts: Take the A30 Exeter to Launceston dual carriageway and exit at the Okehampton turn-off. Once in town, follow the brown tourist signs up the hill to Okehampton Station.

DARTMOUTH STEAM RAILWAY & RIVER BOAT COMPANY

Address: Queen's Park Station, Torbay Road, Paignton TQ4 6AF
Telephone Nº: (01803) 555872
E-mail: carolyn@dsrrb.co.uk
Year Formed: 1973
Location of Line: Paignton to Kingswear
Length of Line: 7 miles

Nº of Steam Locos: 4 (2 in service)
Nº of Other Locos: 6 (2 in service)
Approx Nº of Visitors P.A.: 250,000
Gauge: Standard
Web site: www.dartmouthrailriver.co.uk

GENERAL INFORMATION

Nearest Mainline Station: Paignton (adjacent)
Nearest Bus Station: Paignton (2 minutes walk)
Car Parking: Multi-storey or Mainline Station
Coach Parking: Multi-storey (3 minutes walk)
Souvenir Shop(s): Yes – at Paignton & Kingswear
Food & Drinks: Yes – at Paignton & Kingswear

SPECIAL INFORMATION

A passenger ferry is available from Kingswear Station across to Dartmouth. Combined excursions are also available including train and river trips.

OPERATING INFORMATION

Opening Times: 2019 dates: Open daily from 23rd March to 2nd November and on other dates in February, March and November. Santa Specials operate during dates in December. Please contact the railway for further information.
Steam Working: Trains run throughout the day from 10.30am to 5.00pm.
Prices: Adult Return £18.25 (Includes ferry charge)
  Child Return £11.00 (Includes ferry charge)
  Concession Return £17.25 (Includes ferry)
  Family Return £50.00
  (2 adults and 3 children – Includes ferry charge)
Note: Cheaper fares are charged for shorter journeys

Detailed Directions by Car:
From All Parts: Take the M5 to Exeter and then the A380 to Paignton.

DEAN FOREST RAILWAY

Address: Norchard Centre, Forest Road; Lydney, Gloucestershire GL15 4ET	**Nº of Other Locos**: 18 (3 in service)
Telephone Nº: (01594) 845840	**Nº of Members**: 1,000
Year Formed: 1970	**Annual Membership Fee**: Adult £20.00; Family (4 persons) £25.00; Senior £15.00
Location of Line: Lydney, Gloucestershire	**Approx Nº of Visitors P.A.**: 35,000
Length of Line: 4½ miles	**Gauge**: Standard
Nº of Steam Locos: 7 (2 in service)	**Web site**: www.deanforestrailway.co.uk

GENERAL INFORMATION

Nearest Mainline Station: Lydney (200 metres)
Nearest Bus Station: Lydney Town (400 metres)
Car Parking: 600 spaces at Norchard
Coach Parking: Ample space available
Souvenir Shop(s): Yes + a Museum
Food & Drinks: Operational days only

SPECIAL INFORMATION

Dean Forest Railway preserves the sole surviving line of the Severn and Wye Railway. The Railway has lengthened the line to a total of 4½ miles and Norchard to Parkend is now open for steam train operation giving a round trip of 9 miles.

OPERATING INFORMATION

Opening Times: 2019 dates: Norchard is open daily for viewing. Trains operate on Wednesdays, Saturdays and Sundays from 16th March to 10th November and on various other dates including Santa Specials on most weekends in December. Please contact the railway for further details.

Steam Working: Most services are steam-hauled – check the web site or phone for details. Trains depart Norchard at various times from 10.30am to 3.38pm.

Prices: Adult Return £13.00   OAP Return £12.00
     Child Return £6.00 (Under-5s free)
     Family Ticket £34.00 (2 adults + 2 children)
Note: Fares may differ for Special Events.

Detailed Directions by Car:
From M50 & Ross-on-Wye: Take the B4228 and B4234 via Coleford to reach Lydney. Norchard is located on the B4234, ¾ mile north of Lydney Town Centre; From Monmouth: Take the A4136 and B4431 onto the B4234 via Coleford; From South Wales: Take the M4 then M48 onto the A48 via Chepstow to Lydney; From Midlands/ Gloucester: Take the M5 to Gloucester then the A48 to Lydney; From the West Country: Take the M4 and M48 via the 'Old' Severn Bridge to Chepstow and then the A48 to Lydney.

DERWENT VALLEY LIGHT RAILWAY
(THE BLACKBERRY LINE)

Address: Murton Park, Murton Lane, Murton, York YO19 5UF	**Nº of Steam Locos**: None
Telephone Nº: (01904) 489966	**Nº of Other Locos**: 9
Year Formed: 1991	**Nº of Members**: 170
Location of Line: Murton, near York	**Annual Membership Fee**: £20.00
Length of Line: ½ mile	**Approx Nº of Visitors P.A.**: 12,000
Web site: www.dvlr.org.uk	**Gauge**: Standard
	E-mail: dvlr@hotmail.co.uk

GENERAL INFORMATION

Nearest Mainline Station: York (4 miles)
Nearest Bus Station: York (4 miles)
Car Parking: Large free car park at the site
Coach Parking: Free at the site
Souvenir Shop(s): Yes
Food & Drinks: Available in the Museum.

SPECIAL INFORMATION

The site is the remnants of the Derwent Valley Light Railway which was the last privately owned railway in England, originally opened in 1913.

OPERATING INFORMATION

Opening Times: 2019 dates: Sundays and Bank Holidays from 14th April until 29th September. Open from 11.00am to 4.15pm. Santa Specials also operate on dates in December.
Steam Working: None at present.
Prices: Adult £7.00   Child £5.00
        Senior Citizens/Students £6.00
        Family Tickets £20.00 (2 adult + 2 children)
Note: Prices shown are for entry to the museum. Rides are free thereafter. Prices may be higher on some Special Event days.

Detailed Directions by Car:
From All Parts: The railway is well signposted for the Yorkshire Museum of Farming from the A64 (York to Scarborough road), the A1079 (York to Hull road) and the A166 (York to Bridlington road).

DIDCOT RAILWAY CENTRE

Address: Didcot Railway Centre, Didcot, Oxfordshire OX11 7NJ	**N⁰ of Steam Locos**: 23
Telephone N⁰: (01235) 817200	**N⁰ of Other Locos**: 2
Year Formed: 1961	**N⁰ of Members**: 4,400
Location of Line: Didcot	**Annual Membership Fee**: Please contact the railway centre for details
Length of Line: ¾ mile	**Approx N⁰ of Visitors P.A.**: 70,000
Gauge: Standard and 7 foot ¼ inch	**Web Site**: www.didcotrailwaycentre.org.uk

GENERAL INFORMATION

Nearest Mainline Station:
Didcot Parkway (adjacent)
Nearest Bus Station: Buses to Didcot call at the Railway station
Car Parking: Didcot Parkway car park is adjacent and a new 1,800 space multi-storey car park in Foxhall Road is a longer walk.
Coach Parking: None
Souvenir Shop(s): Yes
Food & Drinks: Yes

SPECIAL INFORMATION

The Centre is based on a Great Western Railway engine shed and is devoted to the re-creation of part of the GWR including Brunel's broad gauge railway and a newly built replica of the Fire Fly locomotive of 1840.

OPERATING INFO

Opening Times: 2019 dates: Weekends all year round, open daily during most school holidays and also from 16th February to 6th October. Weekends and Steam days open 10.30am to 5.00pm. Other days and during the Winter, open 10.30am to 3.30pm.
Steam Working: Bank Holidays and every weekend from 1st June until 1st September. Please phone or check the web site for details of Autumn steam days.
Prices: Adult   £6.50 – £15.00
          Child   £4.50 – £11.00
          Senior Citizen   £6.00 – £13.00
Discounted family tickets are available (2 adults + 2 children) except for Thomas days and other special events. Prices vary depending on the events.

Detailed Directions by Car:
From East & West: Take the M4 to Junction 13 then the A34 and A4130 (follow brown Tourist signs to Didcot Railway Centre); From North: The Centre is signed from the A34 to A4130.

Downpatrick & County Down Railway

Address: Market Street, Downpatrick, Co. Down, Northern Ireland	**Nº of Steam Locos**: 3
Telephone Nº: 028 4461 5779	**Nº of Other Locos**: 5
Year Formed: 1985	**Nº of Members**: 200
Location of Line: Downpatrick	**Annual Membership Fee**: Adult £30.00, Family £70.00, Concessions £20.00
Length of Line: 2 miles	**Approx Nº of Visitors P.A.**: 13,000
Gauge: Irish Standard (5 foot 3 inches)	**Web**: www.downrail.co.uk

GENERAL INFORMATION

Nearest Mainline Station: –
Nearest Bus Station: Adjacent to Station
Car Parking: Ample parking adjacent to Station
Coach Parking: Ample parking adjacent to Station
Souvenir Shop(s): Yes
Food & Drinks: Yes

SPECIAL INFORMATION

This is the only operating Standard (5' 3") Gauge Heritage Railway in Ireland. A carriage Viewing Gallery has recently been opened to enable visitors to get a close-up view of the operations carried out by the Society members.

OPERATING INFORMATION

Opening Times: The Museum is open daily from June to September.
Steam Working: 2019 dates: Easter and May Bank Holiday weekends then weekends from 6th July to 8th September. Also Halloween Ghost Trains on dates in October and Santa and Mince Pie Specials on some dates in December. Please contact the railway for further details. Trains usually run from 2.00pm to 5.00pm.
Prices: Adult Return £7.50
Child Return £5.50   (Under-3's ride free)
Concessionary Return £6.50
Family Return £22.00

Detailed Directions by Car:
From Belfast take the A7 Downpatrick Road. Upon arrival in Downpatrick, follow the brown tourist signs and the Railway Museum is adjacent to the bus station.

EAST ANGLIAN RAILWAY MUSEUM

Address: Chappel & Wakes Colne Station, Colchester, Essex CO6 2DS	**N° of Steam Locos:** 3 **Other Locos:** 2
Telephone N°: (01206) 242524	**N° of Members:** 750
Year Formed: 1969	**Annual Membership Fee:** Adult £22.00; Senior Citizen £20.00
Location of Line: 6 miles west of Colchester on Marks Tey to Sudbury branch	**Approx N° of Visitors P.A.:** 40,000
Length of Line: A third of a mile	**Gauge:** Standard
	Web site: www.earm.co.uk

GENERAL INFORMATION

Nearest Mainline Station: Chappel & Wakes Colne (adajcent)
Nearest Bus Stop: Wakes Colne Post Office (400 yards)
Car Parking: Free parking at site
Coach Parking: Free parking at site
Souvenir Shop(s): Yes
Food & Drinks: Snacks and drinks are available

SPECIAL INFORMATION

The museum has the most comprehensive collection of railway architecture & engineering in the region. The railway also has a miniature railway that usually operates on steam days.

OPERATING INFORMATION

Opening Times: Open daily 10.00am to 4.30pm. Closed on Christmas Day and Boxing Day.
Steam Working: Steam days are held every month from March to August and also in October and December. Bank Holidays are also Steam days. Check the web site for further details.
Prices: Adult £7.00 static viewing; £10.00 Steam
Child £4.00 static viewing; £5.00 Steam
Children under the age of 4 are admitted free of charge. A 10% discount is available for bookings for more than 10 people. A 10% discount is also available for visitors who visit using Mainline trains!

Detailed Directions by Car:
From North & South: Turn off the A12 south west of Colchester onto the A1124 (formerly the A604). The Museum is situated just off the A1124; From West: Turn off the A120 just before Marks Tey (signposted).

EAST KENT RAILWAY

Address: Station Road, Shepherdswell, Dover, Kent   CT15 7PD
Telephone Nº: (01304) 832042
Year Formed: 1985
Location of Line: Between Shepherdswell and Eythorne
Length of Line: 2 miles

Nº of Steam Locos: 2 (1 not in use)
Nº of Other Locos: 7 + 1 DEMU
Nº of Members: 270
Annual Membership Fee: £15.00 (Adult)
Approx Nº of Visitors P.A.: 15,500
Gauge: Standard gauge and also 5 inch and 7¼ inch miniature gauges
Web site: www.eastkentrailway.co.uk

GENERAL INFORMATION

Nearest Mainline Station: Shepherdswell (50 yards)
Car Parking: Available Shepherdswell and Eythorne
Coach Parking: Available at both stations by prior arrangement.
Souvenir Shop(s): Yes
Food & Drinks: Yes – both hot and cold available

SPECIAL INFORMATION

The East Kent Railway was originally built between 1911 and 1917 to service Tilmanstone Colliery. Closed in the mid-1980's, the railway was re-opened in 1995.

OPERATING INFORMATION

Opening Times: The 2019 operating season runs from 6th April until 20th October. Trains operate every Sunday and Bank Holiday during this period plus the last Saturday in July and all Saturdays in August. Also during some other special events including Halloween and Santa Specials. Please contact the railway for details about group bookings: party@eastkentrailway.co.uk
Steam Working: None at present.
Prices: Adult £7.50   Child £3.50 (Under-2s free)
Senior Citizens £5.00
Family £17.50 (2 Adults and 2 Children)

Detailed Directions by Car:
From the A2: Take the turning to Shepherdswell and continue to the village. Pass the shop on the left and cross the railway bridge. Take the next left (Station Road) signposted at the traffic lights for the EKR; From the A256: Take the turning for Eythorne at the roundabout on the section between Eastry and Whitfield. Follow the road through Eythorne. Further on you will cross the railway line and enter Shepherdswell. After a few hundred yards take the right turn signposted for the EKR.

EAST LANCASHIRE RAILWAY

Address: Bolton Street Station, Bury, Lancashire BL9 0EY	**Nº of Steam Locos**: 13
Telephone Nº: (0333) 320-2830	**Nº of Other Locos**: 37
Year Formed: 1968	**Nº of Members**: 3,500
Location of Line: Heywood, Bury, Ramsbottom and Rawtenstall	**Annual Membership Fee**: Adult £23.00; Senior £17.00; Under-18s £11.00
Length of Line: 12 miles	**Approx Nº of Visitors P.A.**: 205,000
	Gauge: Standard
	Web site: www.eastlancsrailway.org.uk

GENERAL INFORMATION

Nearest Mainline Station: Manchester (then Metrolink to Bury)
Nearest Bus Station: ¼ mile
Car Parking: Adjacent
Coach Parking: Adjacent
Souvenir Shop(s): Yes
Food & Drinks: Yes

SPECIAL INFORMATION

Originally opened in 1846, the East Lancashire Railway was re-opened in 1987.

OPERATING INFORMATION

Opening Times: Every weekend & Bank Holiday 9.00am to 5.00pm. Also Wednesday to Friday from 3rd April to 27th September 2019. A number of special events (including Santa Specials) run during the year. Please contact the railway for details.
Steam Working: Most trains are steam-hauled. Saturdays alternate Steam & Diesel. Two engines are in steam on Sundays.
Prices: Adult Return £9.00 – £16.00
Child Return £6.00 – £10.00 (Ages 5 to 17)
Concessionary Return £8.50 – £14.50
Family Return £42.00 (2 Adult + 3 Child)
Cheaper fares are available for shorter journeys.

Detailed Directions by Car:
From All Parts: Exit the M66 at Junction 2 and take the A56 into Bury. Follow the brown tourist signs and turn right into Bolton Street at the junction with the A58. The station is about 150 yards on the right.

EAST SOMERSET RAILWAY

Address: Cranmore Railway Station, Shepton Mallet, Somerset BA4 4QP	**Nº of Steam Locos**: 5
Telephone Nº: (01749) 880417	**Nº of Other Locos**: 5
Year Formed: 1971	**Nº of Members**: 300
Location of Line: Cranmore, off A361 between Frome and Shepton Mallet	**Annual Membership Fee**: £20.00 (Adult)
	Approx Nº of Visitors P.A.: 25,000
Length of Line: 3 miles	**Gauge**: Standard
	Web site: www.eastsomersetrailway.com

GENERAL INFORMATION

Nearest Mainline Station: Castle Cary (10 miles)
Nearest Bus Station: Shepton Mallet (3 miles)
Car Parking: Space for 100 cars available
Coach Parking: Yes
Souvenir Shop(s): Yes
Food & Drinks: Whistlestop Café is open on operating days.

SPECIAL INFORMATION

Footplate experience courses, Sunday lunches, Cream and Sparkling Afternoon Teas are all available for pre-booking as are a number of other family events held throughout the year – phone (01749) 880417 for further details.

E-mail: info@eastsomersetrailway.com

OPERATING INFORMATION

Opening Times: The office and shop are open Tuesday to Friday from 10.00am to 3.30pm when trains are not running (4.30pm on operating days).
Steam Working: 2019 dates: Weekends and Bank Holidays from 30th March to 27th October, Wednesdays from 29th May to 30th October and Thursdays from 25th July to 29th August. Santa Specials run on some December weekends. Special events on other dates. Trains run from 11.00am to 3.30pm.
Prices: Adult Day Rover £10.00
Child Day Rover £8.00
Concessionary Day Rover £9.00
Family Tickets £23.00 and £30.00
Note: Prices are more expensive on Special event days.

Detailed Directions by Car:
From the North: Take A367/A37 to Shepton Mallet then turn left onto A361 to Frome. Carry on to Shepton Mallet and 9 miles after Frome turn left at Cranmore; From the South: Take A36 to Frome bypass then A361 to Cranmore; From the West: Take A371 from Wells to Shepton Mallet, then A361 to Frome (then as above).

ECCLESBOURNE VALLEY RAILWAY

Address: Station Road, Coldwell Street, Wirksworth DE4 4FB
Telephone Nº: (01629) 823076
Year Formed: 2000
Location of Line: Ravenstor to Duffield
Length of Line: 8½ miles

Nº of Steam Locos: 4 (2 operational)
Nº of Other Locos: 12 (including DMUs)
Nº of Members: 700+
Annual Membership Fee: £15.00
Approx Nº of Visitors P.A.: 25,000
Gauge: Standard
Web site: www.e-v-r.com

OPERATING INFORMATION

Opening Times: 2019 dates: Weekends and Bank Holidays from 16th February until 24th November. Also open on Tuesdays from 19th February until 29th October, Thursdays from 30th May until 26th September and Fridays from 5th July to 30st August (as well as during school holidays). Timetables vary depending on the date. Please contact the railway for further details.
Steam Working: Most Weekends and Bank Holidays from 19th April to 8th September except for special Diesel Events.
Prices: Adult Day Rover £14.50
Child Day Rover £7.50
Concessions Day Rover £13.50
Family Day Rover £38.50
Note: Prices vary depending on journey length and discounts are available for advance bookings.

GENERAL INFORMATION

Nearest Mainline Station: Duffield (adjacent)
Nearest Bus Station: Derby (13 miles)
Car Parking: Available at the Station
Coach Parking: Available at Wirksworth Station
Souvenir Shop(s): Yes
Food & Drinks: Yes

SPECIAL INFORMATION

The line was restored section by section and the Railway opened all 8½ miles in April 2011.

Detailed Directions by Car:
From All Parts: Exit the M1 at Junction 26 and take the A610 Ambergate then the A6 to Whatstandwell. Turn left onto the B5035 to Wirksworth and the station is at the bottom of the hill as you enter the town.

ELSECAR HERITAGE RAILWAY

Address: Wath Road, Elsecar, Barnsley, S74 8HJ
Telephone Nº: (01226) 746746
Year Formed: 1997
Location of Line: Elsecar, near Barnsley
Length of Line: 1 mile (increasing to 2 miles when an extension is complete)

Nº of Steam Locos: 4
Nº of Other Locos: 3
Nº of Members: Approximately 160
Annual Membership Fee: £15.00
Approx Nº of Visitors P.A.: 30,000
Gauge: Standard
Web site: www.elsecarrailway.co.uk

GENERAL INFORMATION

Nearest Mainline Station: Elsecar
Nearest Bus Station: Barnsley
Car Parking: Large free car park at the site
Coach Parking: At the site, by arrangement only
Souvenir Shop(s): Yes
Food & Drinks: Yes

SPECIAL INFORMATION

The Railway is based at the Elsecar Heritage Centre which is an antiques and craft centre with a wide range of displays and special events.

OPERATING INFORMATION

Opening Times: The site is open most Mondays, Wednesdays, Thursdays and Saturdays from 10.00am to 4.00pm for static viewing. (closed from 25th December to 2nd January). Trains run on most Sundays and Bank Holidays throughout the year. Hourly services operate from 12.00pm to 2.00pm.
Steam Working: Most services are steam-hauled from April to October. Please phone for further information.
Prices: Adults £5.00   Children £2.50
          Senior Citizens £4.00
Admission to the site is free of charge except for during Special Events.

Detailed Directions by Car:

From All Parts: Exit the M1 at Junction 36 and follow the brown 'Elsecar Heritage' signs taking the A6135 for approximately 2 miles. Turn left onto Broad Carr Road for just under a mile, then right onto Armroyd Lane and right again onto Fitzwilliam Street. Free visitor car parking is available on Wentworth Road off the junction of Fitzwilliam Street and Wath Road.

EMBSAY & BOLTON ABBEY STEAM RAILWAY

Address: Bolton Abbey Station, Bolton Abbey, Skipton, N. Yorkshire BD23 6AF	**N° of Steam Locos**: 14
Telephone N°: (01756) 710614	**N° of Other Locos**: 12
Year Formed: 1968	**N° of Members**: 800
Location of Line: 2 miles east of Skipton	**Annual Membership Fee**: £20.00
Length of Line: 4½ miles	**Approx N° of Visitors P.A.**: 110,000
	Gauge: Standard

GENERAL INFORMATION

Nearest Mainline Station: Skipton (2 miles), Ilkley (3 miles)
Nearest Bus Station: Skipton (2 miles), Ilkley (3 mls)
Car Parking: Large car park at both Stations
Coach Parking: Large coach park at both Stations
Souvenir Shop(s): Yes
Food & Drinks: Yes – Cafe + Buffet cars

SPECIAL INFORMATION

The line extension to Bolton Abbey opened in 1998.

Web site: www.embsayboltonabbeyrailway.org.uk

OPERATING INFORMATION

Opening Times: 2019 dates: Weekends from April to the end of October and daily from 23rd July until 8th September. Tuesdays from April to October and also on some other dates. Santa Specials run on December weekends. Contact the railway for details.
Steam Working: Steam trains depart Embsay Station at 10.30am, 12.00pm, 1.30pm, 3.00pm and 4.30pm on most days during the Main Season. Contact the railway for further details.
Prices: Adult Return £12.00   Child Return £6.00
Concessionary Return £11.00
Family Ticket £30.00 (2 adult + 2 children)
Different fares may apply on special event days.

Detailed Directions by Car:
From All Parts: Embsay Station is off the A59 Skipton bypass by the Harrogate Road. Bolton Abbey Station is off the A59 at Bolton Abbey.

EPPING ONGAR RAILWAY

Address: Ongar Station, Ongar, Essex, CM5 9BN	**Nº of Steam Locos**: 5
Telephone Nº: (01277) 365200	**Nº of Other Locos**: 9
Year Formed: 2004	**Nº of Members**: 600
Location of Line: Epping Forest to Ongar	**Approx Nº of Visitors P.A.**: 40,000
Length of Line: 6.3 miles	**Gauge**: Standard gauge
	Web site: www.eorailway.co.uk

GENERAL INFORMATION

Nearest Mainline Station: Epping Underground – Central line (7½ miles to Ongar Station)
Nearest Bus Station: Epping (7½ miles)
Car Parking: Limited parking close to Ongar Station and plenty of spaces at Epping Station. No parking is available at North Weald Station.
Coach Parking: By arrangement only
Souvenir Shop(s): Yes
Food & Drinks: Available at Ongar and North Weald

SPECIAL INFORMATION

A frequent heritage bus service (number 339) runs from Epping Tube Station (and Shenfield Train Station during the summer) to the railway every operating day. A further bus service (number 381) runs from Epping to North Weald on selected dates.

OPERATING INFORMATION

Opening Times: 2019 dates: Weekends and Bank Holidays from 6th April to 27th October and for Santa Specials during December. Also open on Fridays during the summer school holidays.
Steam Working: Most operating days.
Prices: Adults £14.00
        Children £7.00
        Senior Citizens £13.00
        Family Ticket £36.00

Detailed Directions by Car:
For North Weald Station: Exit the M11 at Junction 7 and follow the A414 towards Chelmsford and North Weald. Take the 3rd exit at the 2nd roundabout ('The Talbot' pub on the left) and follow the road into North Weald village. Station Road is on the left just after leaving the village. For Ongar Station: Exit the M11 at Junction 7 and follow the A414 towards Chelmsford and North Weald. Follow the road for approximately 5 miles going straight on at two roundabouts. At the 3rd roundabout (BP garage on the left) take the third exit towards Ongar. Epping Ongar Railway is located on the right hand side after approximately 400 yards.

FOXFIELD STEAM RAILWAY

Address: Caverswall Road Station, Blythe Bridge, Stoke-on-Trent, Staffs. ST11 9EA
Telephone No: (01782) 396210
Year Formed: 1967
Location of Line: Blythe Bridge
Length of Line: 3½ miles
Gauge: Standard and 7¼ inch miniature

No of Steam Locos: 20 (6 in service)
No of Other Locos: 12
No of Members: Over 300
Annual Membership Fee: Adult £15.00; Junior £6.00; Family £25.00
Approx No of Visitors P.A.: Over 25,000
Web site: www.foxfieldrailway.co.uk

GENERAL INFORMATION

Nearest Mainline Station: Blythe Bridge (¼ mile)
Nearest Bus Station: Hanley (5 miles)
Car Parking: Space for 300 cars available
Coach Parking: Space for 6 coaches available
Souvenir Shop(s): Yes
Food & Drinks: Yes – Buffet and Real Ale Bar

SPECIAL INFORMATION

The Railway is a former Colliery railway built in 1893 to take coal from Foxfield Colliery. It has the steepest Standard Gauge adhesion worked gradient in the UK and freight trains can be seen on these gradients during the annual Steam Gala in July.

OPERATING INFORMATION

Opening Times: 2019 dates: Sundays and Bank Holiday Mondays from 6th April to 27th October. Also Wednesdays from 24th July to 28th August and weekends before Christmas during December. Also, other Special Event days. Open 11.00am to 5.00pm.
Steam Working: Usually 11.30am, 1.00pm, 2.30pm and 4.00pm although Special Event days may run trains at different times.
Prices: Adult Ticket £8.50
        Child Ticket £3.50 (3-16 years old)
        Senior Citizen Ticket £6.50
        Family Ticket £22.00 (2 adult + 2 children)
Note: Fares for Special Events may vary.

Detailed Directions by Car:
From South: Exit M6 at Junction 14 onto the A34 to Stone then the A520 to Meir and the A50 to Blythe Bridge; From North: Exit M6 at Junction 15 then the A500 to Stoke-on-Trent and the A50 to Blythe Bridge; From East: Take the A50 to Blythe Bridge. Once in Blythe Bridge, turn by the Mainline crossing.

GLOUCESTERSHIRE WARWICKSHIRE RAILWAY

Address: The Station, Toddington, Cheltenham, Gloucestershire GL54 5DT	**Nº of Steam Locos:** 9
Telephone Nº: (01242) 621405	**Nº of Other Locos:** 13
Year Formed: 1981	**Nº of Members:** 4,250
Location of Line: 5 miles south of Broadway, Worcestershire, near the A46	**Annual Membership Fee:** £22.00 (Adult)
	Approx Nº of Visitors P.A.: 100,000
Length of Line: 12 miles	**Gauge:** Standard and Narrow gauge
	Web site: www.gwsr.com

GENERAL INFORMATION

Nearest Mainline Station: Cheltenham Spa, Ashchurch or Evesham
Nearest Bus Station: Cheltenham
Car Parking: Parking available at Toddington and Cheltenham Racecourse Stations
Coach Parking: As above, by prior arrangement
Souvenir Shop(s): Yes   **Food & Drinks:** Yes

SPECIAL INFORMATION

The railway has so far restored and reopened 12 miles of line and is in the process of raising £1.5 million to extend the track 3 miles northwards to Broadway. The ultimate aim is to extend a further 6 miles to Honeybourne in the future.

OPERATING INFORMATION

Opening Times: 2019 dates: Weekends 9th March to 3rd November. Tuesday to Thursday 2nd April to 31st October. Santa Specials run at weekends and other dates in December.
Steam Working: Every operating day, though not every service is steam-hauled on most days.
Prices: Adult Day Rover £20.00
    Child Day Rover £8.00
    Senior Citizen Day Rover £19.00
    Family Ticket Day Rover £52.00
        (2 Adults + 3 Children)
    Well-behaved Dogs £3.00
Note: Under 5's travel free of charge apart from on some Special Event days. Tickets are cheaper when purchased in advance.

Detailed Directions by Car:
Toddington is 11 miles north east of Cheltenham, 5 miles south of Broadway just off the B4632 (old A46). Exit the M5 at Junction 9 towards Stow-on-the-Wold for the B4632. The Railway is clearly visible from the B4632.

GREAT CENTRAL RAILWAY

Address: Great Central Station, Great Central Road, Loughborough, Leicestershire LE11 1RW	**Nº of Steam Locos:** 16 (9 in service)
	Nº of Other Locos: 13 + 2 DMUs
	Nº of Members: 5,000
Telephone Nº: (01509) 632323	**Annual Membership Fee:** Adult £25.00;
Year Formed: 1969	Senior £22.00; Junior £15.00
Location: Loughborough to Leicester	**Approx Nº of Visitors P.A.:** 125,000
Length of Line: 8 miles	**Gauge:** Standard
	Web site: www.gcrailway.co.uk

GENERAL INFORMATION

Nearest Mainline Station: Loughborough (1 mile)
Nearest Bus Station: Loughborough (½ mile)
Car Parking: Street parking outside the Station
Coach Parking: Car parks at Quorn & Woodhouse, Rothley and Leicester North
Souvenir Shop(s): Yes
Food & Drinks: Yes – Buffet or Restaurant cars are usually available for snacks or other meals

SPECIAL INFORMATION

The aim of the GCR is to recreate the experience of British main line railway operation during the best years of steam locomotives.

OPERATING INFORMATION

Opening Times: 2019 dates: Weekends throughout the year, Wednesdays from 29th May to 25th September and Tuesdays and Thursdays over the summer holidays. Santa Specials in December and other dates throughout the year. Please contact the railway for further details.
Steam Working: Weekends, Bank Holidays and some Special Events throughout the year.
Prices: Adult Day ticket £18.00
Child Day ticket £9.00
Family Day Ticket £40.00
(2 adults + 3 children)
Family Day Ticket £30.00
(1 adult + 3 children)

Detailed Directions by Car:
Great Central Road is on the South East side of Loughborough and is clearly signposted from the A6 Leicester Road and A60 Nottingham Road.

GREAT CENTRAL RAILWAY (NOTTINGHAM)

Address: Nottingham Transport Heritage Centre, Mere Way, Ruddington, Nottingham   NG11 6NX
Telephone Nº: (0115) 940-5705
Fax Nº: (0115) 940-5905
Year Formed: 1990 (Opened in 1994)
Location of Line: Ruddington to Loughborough Junction

Length of Line: 9 miles
Nº of Steam Locos: 9
Nº of Other Locos: 12
Nº of Members: 750
Annual Membership Fee: £20.00
Approx Nº of Visitors P.A.: 15,000
Gauge: Standard
Web site: www.gcrn.co.uk

GENERAL INFORMATION

Nearest Mainline Station: Nottingham (5 miles)
Nearest Bus Station: Bus service from Nottingham to Ruddington
Car Parking: Available on site (£2.00 charge)
Coach Parking: Free parking at site
Souvenir Shop(s): Yes   **Food & Drinks**: Yes

SPECIAL INFORMATION

The Heritage Centre covers an area of more than eleven acres and is set within the Rushcliffe Country Park in Ruddington. All trains run to Loughborough Junction.

OPERATING INFORMATION

Opening Times: 2019 dates: Weekends and Bank Holidays from 25th May until 1st September. Open 10.45am to 5.00pm. Also open on Sundays in September and October and for Santa Specials on weekends in December.
Steam Working: Steam service runs from 10.45am
Prices: Adult £12.00
         Child £6.00 (Ages 5 to 15)
         Family £30.00 (2 adults + 2 children)
Note: Prices shown above are for unlimited day rover tickets.

Detailed Directions by Car:
From All Parts: The centre is situated off the A60 Nottingham to Loughborough Road and is signposted just south of the traffic lights at Ruddington.

GWILI RAILWAY

Address: Bronwydd Arms Station, Bronwydd Arms, Carmarthen SA33 6HT **Telephone N°**: (01267) 238213 **E-mail**: jjohn@gwili-railway.co.uk **Year Formed**: 1975 **Location of Line**: Near Carmarthen, South Wales **Length of Line**: 5 miles	**N° of Steam Locos**: 7 **N° of Other Locos**: 2 **N° of Members**: 900 shareholders, 380 Society members **Annual Membership Fee**: £18.00 (Adult) **Approx N° of Visitors P.A.**: 28,000 **Gauge**: Standard **Web site**: www.gwili-railway.co.uk

GENERAL INFORMATION

Nearest Mainline Station: Carmarthen (3 miles)
Nearest Bus Station: Carmarthen (3 miles)
Car Parking: Free parking at Bronwydd Arms
Coach Parking: Free parking at Bronwydd Arms
Souvenir Shop(s): Yes
Food & Drinks: Yes

SPECIAL INFORMATION

Gwili Railway was the first Standard Gauge preserved railway in West Wales. There is a riverside picnic area and Miniature railway at Llwyfan Cerrig Station and there is a Signal Box Museum at Bronwydd Arms. A new extension to Abergwili Junction is now operational.

OPERATING INFORMATION

Opening Times: 2019 dates: Open most weekends from 13th April to the end of October, also every Wednesday & Thursday from 17th April to the end of October. Open daily in July and August. Santa Specials operate on December weekends. Please contact the railway for details about Special Events.

Steam Working: All advertised trains are steam hauled. Trains run from 11.00am to 3.00pm.

Prices: Adult £12.00
Child £6.00 (Under-2s ride free of charge)
Family £31.50 (2 adults + up to 2 children)
Senior Citizens £11.00
Dogs £2.00

Note: Discounts are available for larger groups (20+).

Detailed Directions by Car:
The Railway is three miles North of Carmarthen – signposted off the A484 Carmarthen to Cardigan Road.

HEAD OF STEAM – DARLINGTON RAILWAY MUSEUM

Address: North Road Station, Darlington, Co. Durham   DL3 6ST
Telephone Nº: (01325) 405060
Year Formed: 1975
Location of Line: Adjacent to North Road Station
Length of Line: ¼ mile

Nº of Steam Locos: 4
Nº of Other Locos: None
Nº of Members: 800 family memberships
Annual Membership Fee: £10.00 (adult) £15.00 (family);   £10.00 (senior)
Approx Nº of Visitors P.A.: 40,000
Gauge: Standard
Web site: www.head-of-steam.co.uk

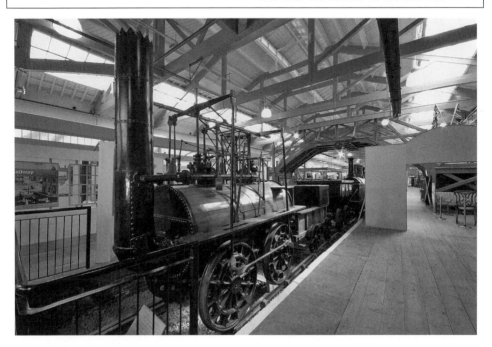

GENERAL INFORMATION

Nearest Mainline Station: North Road (adjacent)
Nearest Bus Station: Darlington (1 mile)
Car Parking: Free parking at site
Coach Parking: Free parking at site
Souvenir Shop(s): Yes
Food & Drinks: Refreshments are available from the reception.

SPECIAL INFORMATION

The museum is an 1842 station on the route of the Stockton and Darlington Railway and is devoted to the Railways of north-east England.

OPERATING INFORMATION

Opening Times: The Museum is open daily throughout the year but is closed every Monday. from April to September and every Monday and Tuesday from October to March. Also closed on Christmas Day, Boxing Day and New Year's Day. Open 10.00am to 4.00pm April to September and from 11.00am to 3.30pm from October to March.
Steam Working: None planned for 2019.
Prices: Adult £4.95
Child £3.00 (ages 5 and under enter free)
Senior Citizen £3.75
Family Ticket £10.00
(2 adults and up to 3 children)

Detailed Directions by Car:
From Darlington Town Centre: Follow the A167 north for about ¾ mile then turn left immediately before the Railway bridge; From A1(M): Exit at Junction 59 then follow A167 towards Darlington and turn right after passing under the Railway bridge.

HELSTON RAILWAY

Address: Trevarno Farm, Prospidnick, Helston, Cornwall TR13 0RY	**N° of Steam Locos**: 2
Contact Telephone N°: 07901 977597	**N° of Other Locos**: 2 (plus 1 DMU)
E-mail: info@helstonrailway.co.uk	**N° of Members**: 6,000 approximately
Year Formed: 2002	**Annual Membership Fee**: £15.00
Location: Trevarno Farm, Helston	**Approx N° of Visitors P.A.**: 4,500
Length of Line: 1 mile	**Gauge**: Standard
	Web site: www.helstonrailway.co.uk

GENERAL INFORMATION

Nearest Mainline Station: Camborne (6 miles)
Nearest Bus Station: Camborne
Car Parking: Free parking at Trevano Farm
Coach Parking: At Trevano Farm
Souvenir Shop(s): Yes
Food & Drinks: Light refreshments are available

SPECIAL INFORMATION

The Helston Railway was formed in 2002 and has reinstated a 1 mile section of track which is open for rides. The long term aim is to reopen a 3 mile section of the line to reach the outskirts of Helston Water-ma-Trout.

OPERATING INFORMATION

Opening Times: Every Thursday, Sunday and Bank Holiday Monday from Easter until November plus extra dates during the school holidays and Santa Specials on December weekends. Please check the website for timetable information. Trains run hourly from 10.30am to 3.30pm.
Steam Working: Selected days during the season. Please contact the railway for details.
Prices: Adults £8.00
Children £5.00
Under-5s ride free of charge
Family Ticket £18.50 (2 adults + 3 children)
Note: Access to the railway is via Trevarno Farm car park where free parking is available.

Detailed Directions by Car:
The railway is situated 1½ miles to the north of Helston, just off the B3303 between Crowntown and Nancegollan.

ISLE OF WIGHT STEAM RAILWAY

Address: The Railway Station, Havenstreet, Near Ryde, Isle of Wight PO33 4DS
Telephone Nº: (01983) 882204
Year Formed: 1971 (re-opened)
Location: Smallbrook Junction to Wootton
Length of Line: 5 miles
Nº of Steam Locos: 12

Nº of Other Locos: 3
Nº of Members: Over 1,000
Annual Membership Fee: £25.00 (Adult)
Approx Nº of Visitors P.A.: 110,000
Gauge: Standard
Talking Timetable: (01983) 884343
Web site: www.iwsteamrailway.co.uk

GENERAL INFORMATION

Nearest Mainline Station: Smallbrook Junction (direct interchange)
Nearest Bus: From Ryde & Newport direct
Car Parking: Free parking at Havenstreet & Wootton Stations
Coach Parking: Free at Havenstreet Station
Souvenir Shop(s): Yes – at Havenstreet Station
Food & Drinks: Yes – at Havenstreet Station

SPECIAL INFORMATION

The IWSR uses mostly Victorian & Edwardian locomotives and carriages to recreate the atmosphere of an Isle of Wight branch line railway.

OPERATING INFORMATION

Opening Times: 2019 dates: Most days in April, May, June and September and daily from 23rd June to 3rd October. Open on Wednesdays, Thursdays and Sundays in October plus Santa Specials on weekends and other dates in December.
Please contact the railway for further information.
Steam Working: 10.05am to 4.20pm (depending on the Station and also the time of year)
Prices: Adult Day Ticket £13.00 – £23.00
Child Day Ticket £6.00 – £11.00
(Under-5s travel free)
Family Day Ticket £32.00 – £57.00
(2 adults + 2 children)
Note: Discounted prices are available for online bookings and First Class tickets are also available.

Detailed Directions by Car:
To reach the Isle of Wight head for the Ferry ports at Lymington, Southampton or Portsmouth. From all parts of the Isle of Wight, head for Havenstreet (which is located 3 miles from Ryde and 3 miles from Newport), and follow the brown tourist signs.

KEIGHLEY & WORTH VALLEY RAILWAY

Address: The Station, Haworth, Keighley, West Yorkshire BD22 8NJ
Telephone Nº: (01535) 645214 (enquiries)
Year Formed: 1962 (Line re-opened 1968)
Location of Line: From Keighley southwards through Haworth to Oxenhope
Length of Line: 4¾ miles

Nº of Steam Locos: 23 **Other Locos**: 12
Members: 5,000 (350 working members)
Annual Membership Fee: Adult £25.00; Adult life membership £491.00
Approx Nº of Visitors P.A.: 120,000
Gauge: Standard
Web Site: www.kwvr.co.uk

GENERAL INFORMATION

Nearest Mainline Station: Keighley (adjacent)
Nearest Bus Station: Keighley (5 minutes walk)
Car Parking: Parking at Keighley, Ingrow, Haworth (charged) and Oxenhope
Coach Parking: At Ingrow & Oxenhope (phone in advance)
Souvenir Shop(s): Yes – at Keighley, Oxenhope & Haworth (whose shop also sells books/DVDs)
Food & Drinks: Yes – at Keighley & Oxenhope when trains run.

SPECIAL INFORMATION

At Ingrow Station, there are two railway museums. Please see www.railstory.co.uk for information.

OPERATING INFORMATION

Opening Times: 2019 dates: Weekends & Bank Holidays throughout the year. Daily from 25th May to 8th September. Also open during the Easter, Whit, February and October School holidays and daily from 26th December to 1st January 2020.
Steam Working: Early trains are Diesel; Steam runs from mid-morning on all operating days including the 4 weekends prior to Christmas when Santa Specials operate (pre-booking necessary for these).
Prices: Adult Return £12.00 (£18.00 Day Rover)
Child Return £6.00 (£9.00 Day Rover)
Small Family Day Rover £22.00 (1 + 1 child)
Concession Day Rover £15.00
Concession Return £11.00

Detailed Directions by Car:
Exit the M62 at Junction 26 and take the M606 to its' end. Follow the ring-road signs around Bradford to Shipley. Take the A650 through Bingley to Keighley and follow the brown tourist signs to the railway. Alternatively, take the A6033 from Hebden Bridge to Oxenhope and follow the brown signs to Oxenhope or Haworth Stations.

THE KEITH & DUFFTOWN RAILWAY

Address: Dufftown Station, Dufftown, Banffshire, AB55 4BA	**Nº of Steam Locos**: None at present
Telephone Nº: (01340) 821181	**Nº of Other Locos**: 6 DMU + 3 shunters
Year Formed: 2000	**Nº of Members**: Approximately 400
Location of Line: Keith to Dufftown	**Annual Membership Fee**: Adult £15.00
Length of Line: 11 miles	**Approx Nº of Visitors P.A.**: Not known
	Gauge: Standard
	Web: www.keith-dufftown-railway.co.uk

GENERAL INFORMATION

Nearest Mainline Station: Keith (½ mile)
Nearest Bus Station: Elgin (Bus routes travel to both Keith and Dufftown)
Car Parking: Available at both Stations
Coach Parking: Available at both Stations
Souvenir Shop(s): Yes – at Keith Town Station
Food & Drinks: Available at Dufftown Station

SPECIAL INFORMATION

The Keith and Dufftown Railway is an eleven mile line linking the World's Malt Whisky Capital, Dufftown, to the market town of Keith. The line, which was reopened by volunteers during 2000 and 2001, passes through some of Scotland's most picturesque scenery, with forest and farmland, lochs and glens, castles and distilleries.

OPERATING INFORMATION

Opening Times: Weekends from Easter until the end of September and also on Fridays from June, to September inclusive. Trains depart Dufftown from 10.30am until 3.30pm.
Steam Working: None at present
Prices: Adult Return £11.00
   Child Return £5.00
   Concessionary Return £9.00
   Family Return £28.00
Note: Shorter journeys are cheaper.

Detailed Directions by Car:
Keith Town Station is located in Keith, on the A96 Aberdeen to Inverness Road; Dufftown Station is about 1 mile to the north of the Dufftown Town Centre just off the A941 road to Elgin.

KENT & EAST SUSSEX RAILWAY

Address: Tenterden Town Station, Tenterden, Kent   TN30 6HE
Telephone Nº: (01580) 765155
Year Formed: 1974
Location of Line: Tenterden, Kent to Bodiam, East Sussex
Length of Line: 10½ miles

Nº of Steam Locos: 12
Nº of Other Locos: 6
Nº of Members: 2,100
Annual Membership Fee: £25.00 (Adult)
Approx Nº of Visitors P.A.: 99,000
Gauge: Standard
Web site: www.kesr.org.uk

GENERAL INFORMATION

Nearest Mainline Station: Headcorn (8 miles)
Nearest Bus Station: Tenterden
Car Parking: Free parking available at Tenterden Town and Northiam Stations
Coach Parking: Tenterden & Northiam
Souvenir Shop(s): Yes
Food & Drinks: Yes

SPECIAL INFORMATION

Built as Britain's first light railway, the K&ESR opened in 1900 and was epitomised by sharp curved and steep gradients and to this day retains a charm and atmosphere all of its own.

OPERATING INFORMATION

Opening Times: 2019 dates: Weekends, Bank Holidays and during school holidays from 6th April to 27th October and also in December. Tuesday to Thursday in May, June, July and September. Daily during August. Also open on other dates. Please check the web site for daily running times and events. Trains depart from 10.40am.
Phone (01580) 762943 for a 24 hour talking-timetable.
Steam Working: Every operational day
Prices: Adult Ticket – £18.00
Child Ticket – £12.00
Family Ticket – £42.00 (2 adult + 2 child)
Well-behaved Dogs allowed – £3.00 each
Note: Prices shown are for All Day travel tickets. First Class upgrades are available for £2.00 (Family Ticket upgrade is £6.50)

Detailed Directions by Car:
From London and Kent Coast: Travel to Ashford (M20) then take the A28 to Tenterden; From Sussex Coast: Take A28 from Hastings to Northiam.

LAKESIDE & HAVERTHWAITE RAILWAY

Address: Haverthwaite Station, near Ulverston, Cumbria   LA12 8AL
Telephone Nº: (015395) 31594
E-mail: info@lakesiderailway.co.uk
Year Formed: 1973
Location of Line: Haverthwaite to Lakeside

Length of Line: 3½ miles
Nº of Steam Locos: 7
Nº of Other Locos: 6
Approx Nº of Visitors P.A.: 190,000
Gauge: Standard
Web site: www.lakesiderailway.co.uk

GENERAL INFORMATION

Nearest Mainline Station: Ulverston (7 miles)
Nearest Bus Station: Haverthwaite (100 yards)
Car Parking: Approximately 150 spaces available – £2.00 charge for all day parking.
Coach Parking: Free parking at site
Souvenir Shop(s): Yes
Food & Drinks: Yes

SPECIAL INFORMATION

Tickets which include train ride followed by a cruise on Lake Windermere or a visit to the Aquarium of the Lakes are also available from the Railway.

OPERATING INFORMATION

Opening Times: 2019 dates: Daily from 30th March to 31st October inclusive. Also open for Santa Specials during weekends from 30th November to 15th December. A number of other Special Events run throughout the year. Please contact the railway for further information.
Steam Working: Daily unless otherwise advertised
Prices: Adult Return £7.10   Single £3.55
        Adult Day Rover £12.00
        Child Return £3.55   Single £2.90
        Child Day Rover £6.00
        Family Ticket £20.50 (2 adult + 3 child)
Note: Prices vary for Special Events and individual fares apply for combined tickets including other attractions.

Detailed Directions by Car:
From All Parts: Exit the M6 at Junction 36 and follow the brown tourist signs.

THE LAVENDER LINE

Address: Isfield Station, Isfield, near Uckfield, East Sussex TN22 5XB	**Nº of Steam Locos:** 3 (1 in service)
Telephone Nº: (01825) 750515	**Nº of Other Locos:** 4 + 2 DEMUs
Year Formed: 1992	**Nº of Members:** Approximately 400
Location of Line: East Sussex between Lewes and Uckfield	**Annual Membership Fee:** Adult £18.00
	Approx Nº of Visitors P.A.: 12,500
Length of Line: 1 mile	**Gauge:** Standard
	Web site: www.lavender-line.co.uk

GENERAL INFORMATION

Nearest Mainline Station: Uckfield (3 miles)
Nearest Bus Station: Uckfield (3 miles)
Car Parking: Free parking on site
Coach Parking: Can cater for coach parties – please contact the Railway.
Souvenir Shop: Yes
Food & Drinks: Yes – Cinders Buffet

SPECIAL INFORMATION

Isfield Station has been restored as a Southern Railway country station complete with the original London Brighton & South Coast Railway signal box.

OPERATING INFORMATION

Opening Times: Sundays and Bank Holidays throughout the year (except for 30th December) plus a number of other Special Event dates including Summer Specials on Thursdays and Fridays in August and Santa Specials in December. Please contact the railway for further details.
Steam Working: Generally, the first and last Sunday of the month April to October inclusive plus some other dates. Contact the railway for further details.
Prices: Adult £10.00
  Child £7.00 (Ages 3 to 15)
  Senior Citizen £8.00
  Family Ticket £30.00 (2 adults + 3 children)
All tickets offer unlimited rides on the day of issue and prices may vary on special event days.

Detailed Directions by Car::
From All Parts: Isfield is just off the A26 midway between Lewes and Uckfield.

LINCOLNSHIRE WOLDS RAILWAY

Address: The Railway Station, Ludborough, Lincolnshire DN36 5SQ
Telephone Nº: (01507) 363881
Year Formed: 1979
Location of Line: Ludborough – off the A16(T) between Grimsby and Louth
Length of Line: 1½ miles

Nº of Steam Locos: 5   **Other Locos:** 7
Nº of Members: 400+
Annual Membership Fee: £36.00 Family, £18.00 Adult, £12.00 Senior Citizen
Approx Nº of Visitors P.A.: 10,000
Gauge: Standard
Web: www.lincolnshirewoldsrailway.co.uk

GENERAL INFORMATION

Nearest Mainline Station: Grimsby (8 miles)
Nearest Bus Stop: Ludborough (½ mile)
Car Parking: Available at Ludborough Station only
Coach Parking: Space for 1 coach only
Souvenir Shop/Museum: Yes
Food & Drinks: Yes

SPECIAL INFORMATION

The LWR operates on a stretch of line which was once part of the Great Northern route from Boston to Grimsby. Heritage steam trains currently run between Ludborough and North Thoresby and work is now in progress to extend the line southwards towards Louth.

E-mail: contact@lincolnshirewoldsrailway.co.uk

OPERATING INFORMATION

Opening Times: 2019 dates: 31st March; 7th plus 19th to 22nd April; 4th to 6th & 25th to 27th May; 16th and 30th June; 7th, 14th, 21st & 28th July; 4th, 7th, 11th, 14th, 18th, 21st, 24th to 26th & 31st August; 1st & 29th September (14th & 15th for static display); 13th & 27th October; 10th & 24th November; Santa Specials (advance booking essential): 14th, 15th, 21st & 22nd December. Also 1st January 2020.
Steam Working: All operating days except 29th September (Diesel Day event).
Prices: Adults £8.00   Children £4.00
       Senior Citizens £6.00
       Family £20.00 (2 adults + 4 children)
Different fares may apply at Special Events.
Otherwise, ticket prices shown offer unlimited rides.

Detailed Directions by Car:
The Railway is situated near Ludborough, ½ mile off the A16(T) Louth to Grimsby road. Follow the brown tourist signs for ½ mile to Fulstow to reach the station. Do not turn into Ludborough but stay on the bypass.

LLANGOLLEN RAILWAY

Address: The Station, Abbey Road, Llangollen, Denbighshire LL20 8SN **Telephone Nº:** (01978) 860979 **Year Formed:** 1975 **Location of Line:** Valley of the River Dee from Llangollen to Corwen **Length of Line:** 10 miles	**Nº of Steam Locos:** 14 **Other Locos:** 13 **Nº of Members:** 1,400 **Annual Membership Fee:** Adult £28.00; Family £39.00; Junior (under-16) £15.00 **Approx Nº of Visitors P.A.:** 110,000 **Gauge:** Standard **Web Site:** www.llangollen-railway.co.uk

Photograph courtesy of D.J. Smith

GENERAL INFORMATION

Nearest Mainline Station: Ruabon (6 miles)
Nearest Bus Station: Wrexham (12 miles)
Car Parking: Llangollen Royal International Pavilion (SatNav post code: LL20 8SW)
Coach Parking: Market Street car park in town centre (SatNav post code: LL20 8PS)
Souvenir Shop(s): Yes – at Llangollen Station
Food & Drinks: Yes – at Llangollen and Carrog and also at Berwyn and Glyndyfrdwy on Gala Days

SPECIAL INFORMATION

The route originally formed part of the line from Ruabon to Barmouth Junction which closed in 1964.

The railway has been rebuilt by volunteers since 1975 and now runs 10 miles through to Corwen.

OPERATING INFORMATION

Opening Times: 2019 dates: Services run daily from 18th February until 10th November. Please check the railway's web site for other out of season opening hours including Santa Specials which operate on weekends and other dates in December.
Steam Working: Please check the web site or contact the railway for details.
Prices: Adult Return £16.00   Child Return £8.50
          Senior Citizen Return £14.50
          Family Return £45.00 (2 adult + 2 child)
Note: Day Rover tickets are also available

Detailed Directions by Car:
From South & West: Go via the A5 to Llangollen. At the traffic lights turn into Castle Street to the River bridge; From North & East: Take the A483 to A539 junction and then via Trefor to Llangollen River bridge. The Station is adjacent to the River Dee. SATNAV use LL20 8SN (but no parking available at the station).

LOCOMOTION

Address: Locomotion, Dale Road, Shildon DL4 2RE	**No of Steam Locos**: 70+ locomotives and other rail vehicles
Telephone Nº: (01904) 685780	**Approx Nº of Visitors P.A.**: 200,000
Year Formed: 2004	**Gauge**: Standard
Location: Shildon, County Durham	**Web site**: www.locomotion.org.uk
Length of Line: Over ½ mile	

GENERAL INFORMATION

Nearest Mainline Station: Shildon (adjacent)
Nearest Bus Station: Durham
Car Parking: Available on site
Coach Parking: Available on site
Souvenir Shop(s): Yes
Food & Drinks: Yes

SPECIAL INFORMATION

A Locomotion you can see highlights of the British National Collection of railway vehicles in the world's first railway town. The museum is home to more than 70 National Rail Collection vehicles, including such icons as 'Sans Pareil', 'APT-E' and the Deltic prototype.

OPERATING INFORMATION

Opening Times: 2019 dates: Open daily but closed from 24th to 26th December and on 1st January. During the winter months (November to March), the Museum is open from 10.00am to 4.00pm. The whole site is open daily during the summer (1st April to 31st October) – 10.00am to 5.00pm.
Steam Working: On special event days – contact the museum or check the web site for further details.
Prices: Admission to the Museum is free of charge.
Train Rides: Adults £3.00
Concessions £2.00

Detailed Directions by Car:
From All Parts: Exit the A1(M) at Junction 58 and take the A68 and the A6072 to Shildon. Follow the Brown tourist signs to Locomotion which is situated ¼ mile to the south-east of the Town Centre.
Drivers using SATNAVs should enter the following post code: DL4 2RE

MANCHESTER MUSEUM OF SCIENCE AND INDUSTRY

Address: Liverpool Road, Manchester, M3 4FP
Telephone Nº: (0161) 832-2244
Year Opened: 1983
Location: Central Manchester

Nº of Steam Locos: A number of locomotives are on display
Approx Nº of Visitors P.A.: –
Gauge: Standard
Web: www.scienceandindustrymuseum.org.uk

GENERAL INFORMATION

Nearest Mainline Station: Deansgate (10 minutes walk)
Nearest Bus Station: Metroshuttle services 1 and 3 stop on Byrom Street, just 5 minutes walk from the museum. Visit www.tfgm.com for information about this free city centre bus service.
Nearest Tram Station (Metrolink): Deansgate-Castlefield is 10 minutes walk.
Car Parking: None available at the museum
Coach Parking: None available at the museum
Souvenir Shop(s): Yes
Food & Drinks: Available in the Museum Café

SPECIAL INFORMATION

The Museum is located at the old Liverpool Road Station, a globally-important site which was the original terminus of the world's first inter-city railway. Visitors can stand in the waiting rooms used by the very first passengers on the Liverpool and Manchester Railway.

OPERATING INFORMATION

Opening Times: Open daily from 10.00am to 5.00pm except for 24th to 26th December. Please check the Museum's web site for details of Special Events.
Prices: Admission is usually free of charge but visitors are invited to make donations. An entrance fee is charged for some Special Events.

Detailed Directions by Car:
The Museum is located in the centre of Manchester. As there are no parking facilities, visitors are advised to use public transport (rail, bus and tram).

MANGAPPS RAILWAY MUSEUM

Address: Southminster Road, Burnham-on-Crouch, Essex CM0 8QG	**N⁰ of Steam Locos**: 6 (1 in service)
Telephone N⁰: (01621) 784898	**N⁰ of Other Locos**: 12
Year Formed: 1989	**Approx N⁰ of Visitors P.A.**: 22,000
Location of Line: Mangapps Farm	**Gauge**: Standard
Length of Line: ¾ mile	**Web site**: www.mangapps.co.uk

GENERAL INFORMATION

Nearest Mainline Station: Burnham-on-Crouch (1 mile)
Nearest Bus Station: –
Car Parking: Ample free parking at site
Coach Parking: Ample free parking at site
Souvenir Shop(s): Yes
Food & Drinks: Yes – drinks and snacks only

SPECIAL INFORMATION

The Railway endeavours to recreate the atmosphere of an East Anglian light railway. It also includes an extensive museum with an emphasis on East Anglian items and signalling.

OPERATING INFORMATION

Opening Times: Closed during January and February then open every weekend and Bank Holiday from the first weekend in March to October inclusive. Also open daily during August. Santa Specials run during weekends in December. Please contact the railway for details of opening times during the School Holidays and for any other information.
Steam Working: Please contact the railway for details of steaming.
Prices: Adult – Steam £9.00; Diesel £8.00
Child – Steam £4.00; Diesel £3.50
Senior Citizen – Steam £8.00; Diesel £7.00
Note: Prices for special events may differ.

Detailed Directions by Car:
From South & West: From M25 take either the A12 or A127 and then the A130 to Rettendon Turnpike and then follow signs to Burnham; From North: From A12 take A414 to Oak Corner then follow signs to Burnham.

THE MIDDLETON RAILWAY

Address: The Station, Moor Road, Hunslet, Leeds LS10 2JQ	**N° of Steam Locos**: 17
Telephone N°: 0845 680-1758	**N° of Other Locos**: 11
Year Formed: 1960	**Annual Membership Fee**: Adults £23.00
Location of Line: Moor Road to Middleton Park	**Approx N° of Visitors P.A.**: 20,000
Length of Line: 1½ miles	**Gauge**: Standard
	Web Site: www.middletonrailway.org.uk
	E-mail: info@middletonrailway.org.uk

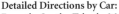

GENERAL INFORMATION

Nearest Mainline Station:
Leeds City (1 mile)
Nearest Bus Station: Leeds (1½ miles)
Car Parking: Free parking at site
Coach Parking: Free parking at site
Souvenir Shop(s): Yes
Food & Drinks: Yes

SPECIAL INFORMATION

The Middleton Railway is the oldest working railway in the world and was established in 1758 by Act of Parliament. The railway is also the first Standard Gauge line to be operated by volunteers and the first revenue-earning steam locomotive ran here in 1812. The railway also hosts a working museum housing a collection of Leeds built locomotives.

OPERATING INFORMATION

Opening Times: 2019 dates: Weekends and Bank Holidays from 6th April to the 27th October plus Santa Specials on weekends in December. Also open on Wednesdays in August. Services run approximately every 40 minutes from 11.00am to 4.00pm.
Steam Working: Diesels usually operate on Saturdays and on Wednesdays in August. All other services are usually steam-hauled including Santa Specials in December.
Prices: Adult £7.00
Child £3.00 (Under-3s ride free)
Family £18.00 (2 adult + 3 child)
Tickets provide for unlimited travel on the day of issue. For a full timetable and details of special events, please check the railway's web site or phone 0845 680-1758.
Note: Different prices may apply on Special Event days.

Detailed Directions by Car:
From the South: Take the M621 Northbound and exit at Junction 5. Turn right at the top of the slip road and take the 3rd exit at the roundabout. The Railway is 50 yards on the right; From the West: Take the M621 Southbound and exit at Junction 6. Turn left at the end of the slip road then left again into Moor Road at the next set of traffic lights. Bear right at the mini roundabout and the railway is on the left after 150 yards.

MID-HANTS RAILWAY (WATERCRESS LINE)

Address: The Railway Station, Alresford, Hampshire SO24 9JG
Telephone Nº: (01962) 733810
Year Formed: 1977
Location of Line: Alresford to Alton
Length of Line: 10 miles

Nº of Steam Locos: 17 (includes 'Thomas')
Nº of Other Locos: 5 + 1 DEMU
Nº of Members: 5,100
Annual Membership Fee: Adult £28.00
Approx Nº of Visitors P.A.: 120,000
Gauge: Standard
Web Site: www.watercressline.co.uk

GENERAL INFORMATION

Nearest Mainline Station: Alton (adjacent) or Winchester (7 miles)
Nearest Bus Station: Winchester or Alton
Car Parking: Pay and display at Alton and Alresford Stations (Alresford free on Sundays & Bank Holidays)
Coach Parking: By arrangement at Alresford Station
Souvenir Shop(s): At Alresford, Ropley & Alton
Food & Drinks: Yes – Buffet on most trains. 'West Country' buffet at Alresford

SPECIAL INFORMATION

Due to a highways improvement scheme, no trains will operate to or from Alton Station until the end of July 2019. Trains will still run from Alresford to Medstead and a free bus service from Alton Station will be provided for passengers for Special Events.

OPERATING INFORMATION

Opening Times: 2019 dates: Weekends and Bank Holidays from 16th March to the end of July plus Tuesday to Thursday from May to July. Please contact the railway for timetable details after July.
Steam Working: All operating days although a Steam/DMU combination is sometimes in service.
Prices: Adult £16.00
Child (ages 5 to 16) £8.00 (Under-5s free)
Family £40.00 (2 adults + 2 children)
Prices shown allow unlimited travel on the day of purchase. Prices may differ on Special Event days. A discount is available for pre-booked parties of 15 or more people. Write or call for a booking form.

Detailed Directions by Car:
From the East: Take the M25 then A3 and A31 to Alton; From the West: Exit the M3 at Junction 9 and take the A31 to Alresford Station.

MID-NORFOLK RAILWAY

Address: The Railway Station, Station Road, Dereham NR19 1DF
Telephone Nº: (01362) 690633
Year Formed: 1995
Location: East Dereham to Wymondham
Length of Line: 11 miles

Nº of Steam Locos: 1 + visiting locos
Nº of Other Locos: 9
Nº of Members: 1,000
Annual Membership Fee: £19.00 (Adult)
Approx Nº of Visitors P.A.: 16,000
Gauge: Standard
Web site: www.mnr.org.uk

GENERAL INFORMATION

Nearest Mainline Station: Wymondham (1 mile)
Nearest Bus Station: Wymondham or East Dereham – each ½ mile away
Car Parking: Available at Dereham Station
Coach Parking: Available at Dereham Station
Souvenir Shop(s): Yes – at Dereham Station
Food & Drinks: Yes – at Dereham Station

SPECIAL INFORMATION

The Mid-Norfolk Railway aims to preserve the former Great Eastern Railway from Wymondham to County School. The section from Wymondham to Dereham was opened to passenger and freight traffic in May 1999 and clearance work is now complete on the East Dereham to County School section.

OPERATING INFORMATION

Opening Times: 2019 dates: Weekends and Bank Holidays from the beginning of April to 13th October. Also on Sundays in March, Wednesdays from May to September and Thursdays from 11th July to the end of August. The Polar Express train rides run on dates in November and December.
Steam Working: Weekends from 4th May to 22nd September and most Wednesdays & Thursdays in July and August. Please check with the railway to confirm before visiting.
Prices: Adult Day Rover £11.00 (£15.00 in Summer)
Child Day Rover £4.00 (£3.00 in Summer)
Senior Citizen Day Rover £10.00 (£12.00 in Summer)
Family Ticket £22.00 (£30.00 in Summer)
Note: First Class tickets are also available.

Detailed Directions by Car:
From All Parts: From the A47 bypass, turn into Dereham and follow the signs for the Town Centre. Turn right at the BP Garage – look out for the brown tourist signs – you will see the Station on your right.

MID-SUFFOLK LIGHT RAILWAY MUSEUM

Address: Brockford Station, Wetheringsett, Suffolk IP14 5PW	**N° of Steam Locos:** 3 **Other Locos:** 2
Telephone N°: (01449) 766899	**N° of Members:** 580
Year Formed: 1990	**Annual Membership Fee:** £12.00
Location of Line: Wetheringsett, Suffolk	**Approx N° of Visitors P.A.:** 6,000
Length of Line: ¼ mile	**Gauge:** Standard
	Web site: www.mslr.org.uk

GENERAL INFORMATION

Nearest Mainline Station: Stowmarket
Nearest Bus Station: Ipswich
Car Parking: Available on site
Coach Parking: Available by prior arrangement
Souvenir Shop(s): Yes
Food & Drinks: Yes

SPECIAL INFORMATION

The Mid-Suffolk Light Railway served the heart of the county for 50 years, despite being bankrupt before the first train ran. In a beautiful rural setting, the Museum seeks to preserve the memory of a unique branch line. The railway is now working on an extension which will more than double the length of the line and plans to open a new destination station, Aspall Halt.

OPERATING INFORMATION

Opening Times: 2019 dates: Open on Sundays and Bank Holiday Mondays from 26th May to 26th August plus a Steam Gala on 7th and 8th September. Santa Specials run on 7th, 8th, 14th, 15th, 21st & 22nd December and on New Year's Day. Open from 11.00am to 5.00pm. Special events may open at different times. Please contact the railway for details.
Steam Working: All operational days. Please contact the railway or check the web site for further information.
Prices: Adult £10.00 Child £5.00 (Under-5s free)
           Family Ticket £25.00 Concession £8.00
Tickets allow unlimited travel on the day of issue and act as season tickets for the calendar year (subject to conditions). Special Event days have higher prices.

Detailed Directions by Car:
The Museum is situated 14 miles north of Ipswich and 28 miles south of Norwich, just off the A140. Look for Mendlesham TV mast and then follow the brown tourist signs from the the A140.

MIDLAND RAILWAY – BUTTERLEY

Address: Butterley Station, Ripley, Derbyshire DE5 3QZ
Telephone Nº: (01773) 747674
Year Formed: 1969
Location of Line: Butterley, near Ripley
Length of Line: Standard gauge 3½ miles, Narrow gauge 0.8 mile

Nº of Steam Locos: 15 (+25 Other Locos)
Nº of Members: 2,000
Annual Membership Fee: £20.00 (Adult)
Approx Nº of Visitors P.A.: 100,000
Gauge: Standard, various Narrow gauges and miniature
Web: www.midlandrailway-butterley.co.uk

GENERAL INFORMATION

Nearest Mainline Station: Alfreton (6 miles)
Nearest Bus Station: Bus stop outside Butterley Station.
Car Parking: Free parking at site – ample space
Coach Parking: Free parking at site
Souvenir Shop(s): Yes – at Butterley and Swanwick
Food & Drinks: Yes – both sites + bar on train

SPECIAL INFORMATION

The Railway is a unique project with a huge Museum development together with narrow gauge, miniature & model railways as well as a country park. Includes an Award-winning Victorian Railwayman's church and Princess Royal Class Locomotive Trust Depot.

OPERATING INFORMATION

Opening Times: 2019 dates: Trains run daily during Easter and Tuesday to Sunday during the School Holidays. Also on most weekends throughout the year and for Santa Specials on dates in November and December. Check the web site for further information. Open from 9.30am to 4.30pm.
Steam Working: Weekends and bank holidays throughout the year and most days in the school holidays. Please phone (01773) 570140 for details.
Prices: Adults £12.50 – £16.50
 Children £6.75 – £8.75
 Family £29.75 – £39.75
 (2 adults + 3 children)
Prices vary depending on the event being run.

Detailed Directions by Car:
From All Parts: From the M1 exit at Junction 28 and take the A38 towards Derby. The Railway is signposted at the junction with the B6179.

NATIONAL RAILWAY MUSEUM – YORK

Address: National Railway Museum, Leeman Road, York YO26 4XJ **Telephone Nº**: 03330 161010 **Year Formed**: 1975 **Location of Line**: York **Length of Line**: Short demonstration line	**Nº of Steam Locos**: 79 **Nº of Other Locos**: 37 **Approx Nº of Visitors P.A.**: 900,000 **Web site**: www.nrm.org.uk **E-mail**: info@railwaymuseum.org.uk

GENERAL INFORMATION

Nearest Mainline Station: York (¼ mile)
Nearest Bus Station: York (¼ mile)
Car Parking: On site long stay car park
Coach Parking: On site
Souvenir Shop(s): Yes
Food & Drinks: Excellent on-site catering facilities.

SPECIAL INFORMATION

The Museum is the greatest of its kind in the world, housing the Nation's collection of locomotives, carriages, uniforms, posters and an extensive photographic archive. Special events and exhibitions run throughout the year. A 7¼ inch miniature railway offers rides in the South Yard area.

OPERATING INFORMATION

Opening Times: Open daily 10.00am to 6.00pm (or 5.00pm during the winter months). Closed from 24th to 26th of December.
Steam Working: School holidays – please phone to confirm details
Prices: Free admission but visitors are invited to make a donation. (Excludes some Special events and Steam rides). Phone 08448 153139 for details.

Detailed Directions by Car:
The Museum is located in the centre of York, just behind the Railway Station. It is clearly signposted from all approaches to York.

NENE VALLEY RAILWAY

Address: Wansford Station, Stibbington, Peterborough PE8 6LR	**No of Steam Locos**: 15
Telephone No: (01780) 784444	**No of Other Locos**: 7
E-mail: nvrorg@nvr.org.uk	**No of Members**: 1,300
Year Formed: 1977	**Annual Membership Fee**: Adult £25.00; Child/Senior £15.00; Family £40.00
Location: Off A1 to west of Peterborough	**Approx No of Visitors P.A.**: 65,000
Length of Line: 7½ miles	**Gauge**: Standard
	Web site: www.nvr.org.uk

GENERAL INFORMATION

Nearest Mainline Station: Peterborough (¾ mile)
Nearest Bus Station: Peterborough (Queensgate – ¾ mile)
Car Parking: Free parking at Wansford & Orton Mere
Coach Parking: Free coach parking at Wansford
Souvenir Shop(s): Yes
Food & Drinks: Yes – at Wansford and Overton

SPECIAL INFORMATION

The railway is truly international in flavour with British and Continental locomotives and rolling stock.

OPERATING INFORMATION

Opening Times: 2019 dates: Most weekends and Bank Holidays from March to December. Also open on most Wednesdays from April to September, most other days in the School summer holidays and at various other times. Santa Specials run in November & December. Please contact the Railway for further details. Trains run from 10.00am to as late as 5.15pm, depending on the time of the year.
Steam Working: Most services are steam hauled apart from on diesel days and times of high fire risk.
Prices: Adult £16.00   Child £8.00 (Under-3s free)
   Family £40.00 (2 adults + 3 children)
   Senior Citizens/Disabled £13.00

Detailed Directions by Car:
The railway is situated off the southbound carriageway of the A1 between the A47 and A605 junctions – west of Peterborough and south of Stamford.

NORTH NORFOLK RAILWAY (THE POPPY LINE)

Address: Sheringham Station, Sheringham, Norfolk   NR26 8RA
Telephone Nº: (01263) 820800
E-mail: enquiries@nnrailway.co.uk
Year Formed: 1975
Location of Line: Sheringham to Holt via Weybourne

Length of Line: 5½ miles
Nº of Steam Locos: 5 (+ visiting locos)
Nº of Other Locos: 4
Approx Nº of Visitors P.A.: 166,000
Gauge: Standard
Web site: www.nnrailway.co.uk

GENERAL INFORMATION

Nearest Mainline Station: Sheringham (200 yards)
Nearest Bus Station: Outside the Station
Car and Coach Parking:
Adjacent to Sheringham and Holt
Souvenir Shop(s): Available at all stations
Food & Drinks: Yes – main catering facilities at Sheringham Station. Light refreshments elsewhere.

SPECIAL INFORMATION

Lunch and evening dinner trains are scheduled throughout the year. Please check the website for times and fares. Weybourne Station is licensed for weddings.

OPERATING INFORMATION

Opening Times: 2019 dates: Daily from 30th March to 3rd November. Also during weekends in March and November with Santa specials running during December. A number of other Special Events are held throughout the year. Please check the railway's web site for further details.
Steam Working: 9.55am to 5.00pm (during high season)
Prices: Adult £13.50
         Child £9.75   (Under-5s travel free)
         Family £45.50 (2 adults + 2 children)
         Senior Citizens £12.50
         Dogs and Bicycles £2.00 each
The prices shown above are for all-day hop-on, hop-off, Day Rover tickets.
Special Events may have different prices.

Detailed Directions by Car:
Sheringham Station is situated just off the A149. Holt Station is located at High Kelling, just off the A148.

NORTH TYNESIDE STEAM RAILWAY

Address: Stephenson Railway Museum, Middle Engine Lane, North Shields, NE29 8DX	**No of Steam Locos**: 4
	No of Other Locos: 3
	No of Members: 30
Telephone No: (0191) 200-7146	**Annual Membership Fee**: Adult £12.00
Year Formed: 1986	**Approx No of Visitors P.A.**: 46,000
Location: Stephenson Railway Museum	**Gauge**: Standard
Length of Line: 1½ miles	**Web site**: www.ntsra.org.uk

GENERAL INFORMATION

Nearest Mainline Station: Newcastle Central (5 miles) or for the Metro Percy Main (1½ miles)
Nearest Bus Station: North Shields
Car Parking: Free parking available on site
Coach Parking: Free parking available on site
Souvenir Shop(s): Yes
Food & Drinks: None

SPECIAL INFORMATION

A programme of events and activities is available from the Museum on request. Use the following URL:

www.twmuseums.org.uk/stephenson

OPERATING INFORMATION

Opening Times: 2019 dates: Sundays and Bank Holidays from Easter to October half-term and daily during the School Holidays, 11.00am to 4.00pm.
Steam Working: Sundays and Bank Holiday Mondays from June to September.
Prices: Adult Day Rover £6.00
Child/Concessionary Day Rover £4.00
Family Day Rover £15.00
(2 Adults + 2 Children)
A voluntary donation of £1.00 can be added to the cost of tickets (£2.00 for Family Tickets).
Note: Admission to the museum is free of charge and Season Tickets are also available.

Detailed Directions by Car:
The Railway is adjacent to the Silverlink Retail Park approximately ½ mile from the junction between the A19 and A1058. From the A19/A1058 junction look for the signs for 'Silverlink' before following the Brown tourist signs to the Stephenson Railway Museum.

NORTH YORKSHIRE MOORS RAILWAY

Address: Pickering Station, Pickering, North Yorkshire YO18 7AJ	**N° of Other Locos:** 10
Telephone N°: (01751) 472508 (enquiries)	**N° of Members:** 9,600
Year Formed: 1967	**Annual Membership Fee:** Adult £31.00; Senior £29.00; Junior £15.00
Location of Line: Pickering to Grosmont via stations at Levisham and Goathland	**Approx N° of Visitors P.A.:** 350,000
Length of Line: 18 miles	**Gauge:** Standard
N° of Steam Locos: 16	**Web site:** www.nymr.co.uk
	E-mail: info@nymr.co.uk

GENERAL INFORMATION

Nearest Mainline Station: Grosmont or Whitby
Nearest Bus Station: Pickering (½ mile)
Car Parking: Available at each station
Coach Parking: None
Souvenir Shop(s): Yes – at Pickering, Goathland, and Grosmont Stations plus Grosmont MPD
Food & Drinks: Pickering, Grosmont & Goathland. Also at Levisham on weekends and bank holidays.

SPECIAL INFORMATION

The NYMR runs through the spectacular North York Moors National Park and is the most popular heritage railway in the country. As seen in 'Heartbeat' and the first Harry Potter film. The railway operates extended services to and from Whitby.

OPERATING INFORMATION

Opening Times: 2019 dates: Open daily from 30th March to 3rd November and a Winter Timetable will then operate from 26th December 2019 to 1st January 2020 and February 2020 half-term. Santa Specials operate on weekends in December.
Steam Working: Locomotive allocations are made each evening after a fit to run test and scheduled locomotives for the following day are posted on the web site at the earliest opportunity.
Prices: Adult Day Rover £26.00 – £33.00
Child Day Rover £13.00 – £16.50
Family Day Rover Tickets £54.00 – £68.00
(2 adults and 2 or 3 children options)

Detailed Directions by Car:
From the South: Follow the A64 past York to the Malton bypass then take the A169 to Pickering; From the North: Take A171 towards Whitby then follow the minor road through Egton to Grosmont.

NORTHAMPTON & LAMPORT RAILWAY

Address: Pitsford & Bramford Station, Pitsford Road, Chapel Brampton, Northampton NN6 8BA
Telephone Nº: (01604) 820327 (infoline)
Year Formed: 1983 (became operational in November 1995)
Length of Line: 1½ miles at present

Nº of Steam Locos: 5 **Nº Other Locos:** 6
Nº of Members: 350
Annual Membership Fee: Adult £20.00; Senior Citizen £15.00; Under-16 £10.00
Approx Nº of Visitors P.A.: 9,300
Gauge: Standard
Web site: www.nlr.org.uk

GENERAL INFORMATION

Nearest Mainline Station: Northampton (5 miles)
Nearest Bus Station: Northampton (5 miles)
Car Parking: Free parking at site
Coach Parking: Free parking at site
Souvenir Shop(s): Yes
Food & Drinks: Yes

SPECIAL INFORMATION

The railway operates on a section of the old London & North Western Railway line between Northampton and Market Harborough and became operational again on 18th November 1995. Work is currently underway on a southern extension to the line.

OPERATING INFORMATION

Opening Times: 2019 dates: Most Sundays and Bank holidays from 24th March until 13th October and Santa Specials on most weekends in December. Open from 10.30am to 4.30pm (the last train runs at 3.30pm). Please contact the railway for a more detailed timetable.
Steam Working: Bank Holiday weekends and Santa Specials in December. Steam and Diesel trains run on alternating Sundays during other times. Please contact the railway for further information.
Prices: Adult £5.20
Child £4.20 (Under-2s ride free)
Family £16.20 (2 adults + 2 children)
Senior Citizen £4.20
Fares may vary on Special Event days.

Detailed Directions by Car:
The station is situated along the Pitsford road at Chapel Brampton, approximately 5 miles north of Northampton. Heading north out of town, it is signposted to the right on the A5199 (A50) Welford Road at Chapel Brampton crossroads or on the left on the A508 Market Harborough road at the Pitsford turn.

PEAK RAIL PLC

Address: Matlock Station, Matlock, Derbyshire DE4 3NA	**N° of Steam Locos**: 4 **Other Locos**: 40+
Telephone N°: (01629) 580381	**N° of Members**: 1,500
Fax N°: (01629) 760645	**Annual Adult Membership Fee**: £16.00
Year Formed: 1975	**Approx N° of Visitors P.A.**: 150,000
Location: Matlock to Rowsley South	**Gauge**: Standard
Length of Line: Approximately 4½ miles	**Web site**: www.peakrail.co.uk
	E-mail: peakrail@peakrail.co.uk

GENERAL INFORMATION

Nearest Mainline Station: Matlock
Nearest Bus Station: Matlock
Car Parking: Paid car parking at Matlock Station. 200 free parking spaces available at Rowsley South Station and 20 free spaces at Darley Dale Station
Coach Parking: Free parking at Rowsley South
Souvenir Shop(s): Yes
Food & Drinks: Yes – R.M.B. Buffet on the train and the Rowsley Buffet at Rowsley South Station.

SPECIAL INFORMATION

The Palatine Restaurant Car is often available whilst travelling on the train, catering for Sunday Lunches, Teas and Party Bookings (please check with the Railway for operating dates for the Palatine). Coach parties are welcomed when the railway is operating.

OPERATING INFORMATION

Opening Times: 2019 dates: Weekends and Bank Holidays throughout the year from 16th February onwards. Also Tuesdays and Wednesdays from mid-April to the end of August and Tuesdays in September. Santa Specials run during weekends in December. Please contact the railway for further information. First departure from Rowsley South Station is 11.00am, last train departs at 3.56pm.
Steam Working: All services throughout the year.
Prices: Adult £9.50
  Children – Ages 3-15 £4.50 (Under-3s free)
  Senior Citizen £8.00
  Family Ticket £30.50
    (2 adults + 3 children)
Note: Tickets allow unlimited travel on the day of purchase.

Detailed Directions by Car:
Exit the M1 at Junctions 28, 29 or 30 and follow signs towards Matlock. From North and South take A6 direct to Matlock. From Stoke-on-Trent, take the A52 to Ashbourne, then the A5035 to Matlock. Upon reaching Matlock follow the brown tourist signs.

PLYM VALLEY RAILWAY

Address: Marsh Mills Station, Coypool Road, Plympton, Plymouth PL7 4NW	**Nº of Steam Locos**: 4
Telephone Nº: (01752) 345078	**Nº of Other Locos**: 4
Year Formed: 1980	**Nº of Members**: 250
Location of Line: Marsh Mills to Plym Bridge Platform	**Annual Membership Fee**: £1400
	Approx Nº of Visitors P.A.: 5,000
Length of Line: 1½ miles	**Gauge**: Standard
	Web site: www.plymrail.co.uk

GENERAL INFORMATION

Nearest Mainline Station: Plymouth (4 miles)
Nearest Bus Station: Plymouth (3 miles)
Car Parking: Available at the Park & Ride opposite the main gates to the railway
Coach Parking: As above
Souvenir Shop(s): Yes
Food & Drinks: Light snacks available

SPECIAL INFORMATION

2012 saw the opening of the extension of the line to Plym Bridge. This is a section of the former Great Western branch line which from Tavistock Junction through to Launceston. The railway now plans to further develop their visitor facilities at Marsh Mills.

OPERATING INFORMATION

Opening Times: Open for static viewing on most Sundays from 11.00am to 5.00pm and brake van rides are also available on most Sundays from March to mid-November except when trains are running. Trains run on a number of dates throughout the year including the 'North Pole Express' on December weekends (advance bookings required). Please check with the railway for further details of these and other Special Events.
Steam Working: Please contact the railway for details.
Prices: Adult Return £5.00   Day Rover £8.00
         Child Return £2.00   Day Rover £3.00
Note: There is no charge to visit the station.

Detailed Directions by Car:
Leave the A38 at the Marsh Mills turn-off and take the B3416 towards Plympton. Turn left into Coypool Road just after the McDonalds restaurant. From Plymouth City Centre, take the A374 to Marsh Mills, then as above.

PONTYPOOL & BLAENAVON RAILWAY

Address: 33 Broad Street, Blaenavon, Torfaen NP4 9ND
e-mail: info@pbrly.co.uk
Telephone Nº: (01495) 792263 (Shop)
Year Formed: 1980 (Opened 1983)
Location of Line: Just off the B4248 between Blaenavon and Brynmawr
Length of Line: 3½ miles

Nº of Steam Locos: 2
Nº of Other Locos: 1
Nº of Members: 350
Annual Membership Fee: £15.00
Approx Nº of Visitors P.A.: 16,500
Gauge: Standard
Web site:
www.pontypool-and-blaenavon.co.uk

GENERAL INFORMATION

Nearest Mainline Station: Abergavenny (5 miles)
Nearest Bus Station: Blaenavon Town (1½ miles) – regular bus service within ¼ mile (except Sundays)
Car Parking: Free parking for 50 cars on site
Coach Parking: Available on site
Souvenir Shop(s): Yes – at the Station and also a shop at 33 Broad Street, Blaenavon
Food & Drinks: Light refreshments on the train and at the station.

SPECIAL INFORMATION

The railway operates over very steep gradients, is run entirely by volunteers and is the highest standard gauge preserved railway in England and Wales.

OPERATING INFORMATION

Opening Times: 2019 dates: Every weekend and Bank Holiday Monday from 6th April to 29th September. Also 26th, 27th, 30th & 31st October, Wednesdays from 7th to 28th August and Santa Specials on weekends in December. Please check the web site for further details.
Steam Working: Trains are steam-hauled during Peak days and special steam days during May and June. Diesel locos may be used on quiet days. Please contact the Railway for further information.
Prices: Adult Day Rover £9.00 (Concessions £8.00)
    Child Day Rover £5.00
    Family Day Rover £23.00 (2 adult + 3 child)
Note: Fares may vary on Special Event days.

Detailed Directions by Car:
From All Parts: The railway is situated just off the B4248 between Blaenavon and Brynmawr and is well signposted as you approach Blaenavon. Use Junction 25A if using the M4 from the East, or Junction 26 from the West. Head for Pontypool. From the Midlands use the M50, A40 then A465 to Brynmawr. From North & West Wales consider using the 'Heads of the Valleys' A465 to Brynmawr. As you approach the Railway, look out for the Colliery water tower – you can't miss it!

RIBBLE STEAM RAILWAY

Address: Chain Caul Road, Preston, PR2 2PD
Telephone Nº: (01772) 728800
Year Formed: 2005
Location: West of Preston City Centre
Length of Line: 3 mile round trip

Nº of Steam Locos: 40
Nº of Other Locos: 21
Nº of Members: 400
Annual Membership Fee: £15.00
Approx Nº of Visitors P.A.: 20,000+
Gauge: Standard
Web site: www.ribblesteam.org.uk

GENERAL INFORMATION

Nearest Mainline Station: Preston (2 miles)
Nearest Bus Station: Preston (2 miles)
Car Parking: Available on site
Coach Parking: Available on site
Souvenir Shop(s): Yes
Food & Drinks: Available

SPECIAL INFORMATION

The line traverses a swing bridge across the Marina entrance – the only preserved steam line in Britain to have such a feature! The railway also has the largest collection of standard gauge industrial locomotives housed under cover in the UK.

OPERATING INFORMATION

Opening Times: 2019 dates: Open 10.30am to 5.00pm on dates in April then weekends and Bank Holidays from 12th May to 21st September. Also open for Santa specials on weekends in December. Please contact the railway for details of further operating days.

Steam Working: On all days when the railway is open to the public. Trains run hourly from 11.00am to 4.00pm.

Prices: Adult Return £7.00
　　　　　Child/Concessionary Return £4.50
　　　　　Family Return £20.00

Note: Special event prices may differ to those shown.

Detailed Directions by Car:

From All Parts: The Railway is located on the Riversway/Docklands Business and Residential Park, just off the A583 Lytham/Blackpool road and approximately 1½ miles to the west of Preston City Centre. Follow the Brown Tourist signs from the A583 for the railway.

ROCKS BY RAIL –
THE LIVING IRONSTONE MUSEUM

Address: Ashwell Road, Cottesmore, Oakham, Rutland LE15 7FF	**Nº of Steam Locos:** 12
Telephone Nº: 07974 171068	**Nº of Other Locos:** 12
Year Formed: 1979	**Nº of Members:** 275
Location of Line: Between the villages of Cottesmore and Ashwell	**Annual Membership Fee:** £10.00
Length of Line: ¾ mile	**Approx Nº of Visitors P.A.:** 8,000
	Gauge: Standard
	Web site: www.rocks-by-rail.org

GENERAL INFORMATION

Nearest Mainline Station: Oakham (4 miles)
Nearest Bus Station: Cottesmore/Ashwell (1½ miles)
Car Parking: Available at the site
Coach Parking: Limited space available
Souvenir Shop(s): None
Food & Drinks: Available on Thursdays and many Sundays from Easter to October.

SPECIAL INFORMATION

This Industrial Railway Heritage centre is located at the end of the former Ashwell-Cottesmore mineral branch and is based at the former exchange sidings.

OPERATING INFORMATION

Opening Times: 2019 dates: Static viewing on Tuesdays and Thursdays from 10.00am to 4.00pm throughout the year plus many Sundays from Easter to November. Also open with the 'Driver for a Fiver' offer (Diesel locomotive) on the second Sunday of each month during this period plus quarry demonstration working days on Bank Holiday Mondays.
Steam Working: 3rd Sunday each month, Easter to November, with brake van rides 10.00am to 3.30pm.
Prices: Adults £10.00   Children £6.00 (age 3-14)
Concessions £8.00
Family Ticket £30.00 (2 adults + 3 children)

Detailed Directions by Car:
From All Parts: The Museum is situated 4 miles north of Oakham between Ashwell and Cottesmore. Follow the brown tourist signs from the B668 Oakham to A1 road or the signs from the A606 Stamford to Oakham Road.

ROYAL DEESIDE RAILWAY

Address: Milton of Crathes, Crathes, Banchory AB31 5QH	**No of Steam Locos:** 3
Telephone No: (01330) 844416	**No of Other Locos:** 3 + 1 BMU
E-mail: info@deeside-railway.co.uk	**No of Members:** 250
Year Formed: 1996	**Annual Membership Fee:** £20.00
Location of Line: Milton of Crathes	**Approx No of Visitors P.A.:** 12,000
Length of Line: 1 mile	**Gauge:** Standard
	Web site: www.deeside-railway.co.uk

GENERAL INFORMATION

Nearest Mainline Station: Aberdeen (14 miles)
Nearest Bus Station: Stagecoach Bluebird bus stop nearby on A93.
Car Parking: Free parking available on site
Coach Parking: Free parking available on site
Souvenir Shop(s): Yes
Food & Drinks: Yes – inside the restored Victorian station and also inside a static catering car.

SPECIAL INFORMATION

The line is gradually being extended to Banchory and, when completed, will be 2 miles in length.

OPERATING INFORMATION

Opening Times: 2019 dates: Sundays from 31st March to 20th October plus Bank Holidays and some weekends in April, July and August and Wednesdays from 10th July to 14th August. Also open for Santa Specials each weekend in December and the last weekend in November. Please contact the railway for further information.
Steam Working: Please contact the railway for details of steaming dates.
Prices: Adult Day Rover £7.50
              Child Day Rover £4.00 (Under-3s free)
              Senior Citizen Day Rover £5.00
              Family Day Rover Ticket £20.00
                          (2 adults + 3 children)

Detailed Directions by Car:
From the South: Take the A90 to Stonehaven. Exit onto the B979 for Stonehaven and follow into the town square. Turn left at the traffic lights and follow signs for the A957 to Banchory (Historic Slug Road). Follow this road for 14 mile via Durris to Crathes and the junction with the A93. Turn left and follow the Brown Tourist signs, turning left for the railway after approximately 600 yards; From the North & West: Follow the A980 to Banchory and turn left onto the A93. Turn right following the Brown Tourist signs for the railway.

RUSHDEN TRANSPORT MUSEUM & RAILWAY

Address: Rushden Station, Station Approach, Rushden, NN10 0AW	**Nº of Steam Locos:** 3
Telephone Nº: (01933) 353111	**Nº of Other Locos:** 5
Year Formed: 1985	**Nº of Members:** Approximately 650
Location of Line: Rushden, Northants.	**Annual Membership Fee:** £25.00
Length of Line: ½ mile (each paid trip is 2½ miles in distance)	**Approx Nº of Visitors P.A.:** 5,000
	Gauge: Standard
	Web site: www.rhts.co.uk

GENERAL INFORMATION

Nearest Mainline Station: Wellingborough (5 miles)
Nearest Bus Station: Northampton (14 miles)
Car Parking: Available on site. On operating days a nearby public car park must be used.
Coach Parking: None
Souvenir Shop(s): Yes
Food & Drinks: Available on operating weekends

SPECIAL INFORMATION

The Rushden Transport Museum is situated in the old Midland Railway Station of 1894 which once formed part of the Wellingborough to Higham Ferrers branch line. Taken over by the Rushden Historical Transport Society in 1984 the station also provides the society with a social club.

OPERATING INFORMATION

Opening Times: The Museum is open from Easter until the end of October on Saturdays (2.00pm to 4.00pm), Sundays (11.00am to 4.00pm) and most Fridays (2.00pm to 4.00pm). A variety of special events are scheduled for 2019. For further details, either check the museum's web site or phone for information.
Steam Working: Trains are operated by The Rushden, Higham & Wellingborough Railway at various events throughout the year. Please contact the museum for further details.
Prices: Admission to the museum is usually free but charges will be made on Special Event days.

Detailed Directions by Car:
From All Parts: Take the A6 to the Rushden Bypass (to the south of the A45) and turn into John Clark Way by the large grey warehouses. The Station is located on the right-hand side of the road after approximately 400 yards.

SCOTTISH INDUSTRIAL RAILWAY CENTRE

Address: Dunaskin, Dalmellington Road, Waterside, Patna, Ayrshire KA6 7JF	**Nº of Steam Locos**: 7
Telephone Nº: (01292) 313579 (Evenings & Weekends)	**Nº of Other Locos**: 10
	Nº of Members: 180
	Annual Membership Fee: £20.00
Year Formed: 1974	**Approx Nº of Visitors P.A.**: 3,500
Location of Line: Dunaskin Ironworks	**Gauge**: Standard
Length of Line: One third of a mile	
Web site: www.scottishindustrialrailwaycentre.org.uk	
E-mail: info@scottishindustrialrailwaycentre.org.uk	

GENERAL INFORMATION

Nearest Mainline Station: Ayr (10 miles)
Nearest Bus Station: ½ hourly bus service from Ayr – phone (01292) 613500 for more information
Car Parking: Free parking available at the site
Coach Parking: Free parking available at the site
Souvenir Shop(s): Yes
Food & Drinks: Cafe available on site

SPECIAL INFORMATION

The Railway is operated by the Ayrshire Railway Preservation Group and is located at the very last engine shed to be built in the UK to service steam locomotives, constructed in 1964.

OPERATING INFORMATION

Opening Times: 2019 operating dates: Selected Sundays from May to September. Open 11.00am to 4.30pm on these days (last admission at 4.00pm). The site is closed at all other times. Please contact the railway or check the web site for further details.
Steam Working: On all operating dates.
Prices: Adults £7.00
   Children £4.00 (Free for ages 3 and under)
   Senior Citizens £4.00
   Family Ticket £18.00 (2 adults + 3 children)

Detailed Directions by Car:
From All Parts: Dunaskin is situated adjacent to the A713 Ayr to Castle Douglas road, approximately 10 miles to the southwest of Ayr.

SEVERN VALLEY RAILWAY

Correspondence Address: Number One Comberton Place, Kidderminster DY10 1QR **Telephone Nº:** (01562) 757900 **Year Formed:** 1965 **Location of Line:** Kidderminster (Worcs.) to Bridgnorth (Shropshire) **Length of Line:** 16 miles	**Nº of Steam Locos:** 29 (9 in service) **Nº of Other Locos:** 26 **Nº of Members:** 12,000+ **Annual Membership Fee:** Adult £22.00 **Approx Nº of Passengers P.A.:** 250,000 **Gauge:** Standard **Web site:** www.svr.co.uk

GENERAL INFORMATION

Nearest Mainline Station: Kidderminster (adjacent)
Nearest Bus Station: Kidderminster (500 yards)
Car Parking: Large car park at Kidderminster. Spaces also available at other stations.
Coach Parking: At Kidderminster
Souvenir Shop(s): At Kidderminster & Bridgnorth
Food & Drinks: On most trains. Also at Bewdley, Bridgnorth, Kidderminster and The Engine House

SPECIAL INFORMATION

The SVR has numerous special events including an Autumn Steam Gala, 1940's weekend, Classic Car & Bike Day and visits by Santa! 'The Engine House', the railway's visitor and education centre, is a further attraction at Highley.

OPERATING INFORMATION

Opening Times: 2019 dates: Weekends from mid-February to the end of November. Also daily from 13th April to 29th September and during local School Holidays. Santa Specials run at weekends and on some other dates in December. Please contact the railway for further details.
Steam Working: Train times vary depending on timetable information. Phone for details.
Prices: Adult Day Rover £22.00
              Child Day Rover £14.50
              Senior Citizen Day Rover £22.00
Note: Entrance to The Engine House is included in the above prices and upgrades to First Class travel are also available. Discounts are available for advance bookings. Family Tickets are also available.

Detailed Directions by Car:
For Kidderminster exit the M5 at Junction 3 or Junction 6 and follow the brown tourist signs for the railway; From the South: Take the M40 then M42 to Junction 1 for the A448 to Kidderminster.   SATNAV DY10 1QX

SOMERSET & DORSET RAILWAY TRUST MUSEUM

Address: The Railway Station, Washford, Somerset TA23 0PP	**Nº of Steam Locos:** 2
	Nº of Other Locos: 1
Telephone Nº: (01984) 640869	**Annual Membership Fee:** £14.00
Year Formed: 1966	**Approx Nº of Visitors P.A.:** 3,000
Location of Line: Washford Station	**Gauge:** Standard
Length of Line: Station sidings only	**Web site:** www.sdrt.org.uk

GENERAL INFORMATION

Nearest Mainline Station: Taunton (17 miles)
Nearest Bus Station: Taunton (17 miles)
Car Parking: Available on site
Coach Parking: None
Souvenir Shop(s): Yes
Food & Drinks: None

SPECIAL INFORMATION

The Museum of the Somerset & Dorset Railway Trust contains a mass of exhibits about and memorabilia of this much loved line. This includes a reconstruction of Midford signal box and carriages and wagons including some undergoing restoration.

OPERATING INFORMATION

Opening Times: A full list of opening dates had not been set at the time of going to press. Please check the Museum's web site or phone for further details.
Steam Working: Please contact the Museum or check the web site for further details.
Prices: Admission to the Museum –
   Adult £2.00
   Child £1.00
   Family £5.00
Note: Additional charges may apply on Special Event days.

Detailed Directions by Car:
The Museum is located at the Railway Station in Washford Village on the A39 Bridgwater to Minehead road.

SOUTH DEVON RAILWAY

Address: Buckfastleigh Station, Buckfastleigh, Devon TQ11 0DZ	**N° of Steam Locos:** 15 (4 in service)
Telephone N°: 01364 644370	**N° of Other Locos:** 11
Year Formed: 1969	**N° of Members:** 2,500
Location of Line: Totnes to Buckfastleigh via Staverton	**Annual Membership Fee:** £22.00 Adult
	Approx N° of Visitors P.A.: 100,000+
	Gauge: Standard
Length of Line: 7 miles	**Web Site:** www.southdevonrailway.co.uk

GENERAL INFORMATION

Nearest Mainline Station: Totnes (¼ mile)
Nearest Bus Station: Totnes (½ mile), Buckfastleigh (Station Road)
Car Parking: Free parking at Buckfastleigh, Council/NR parking at Totnes
Coach Parking: As above
Souvenir Shop(s): Yes – at Buckfastleigh
Food & Drinks: Yes – at Buckfastleigh & on train

SPECIAL INFORMATION

The railway was opened in 1872 as the Totnes, Buckfastleigh & Ashburton Railway.

OPERATING INFORMATION

Opening Times: 2019 dates: Daily from 16th March to 3rd November. Santa Specials also run on weekends and other dates during December. Please contact the railway for further details.
Steam Working: Almost all trains are steam hauled.
Prices: Adult Return £16.00
　　　　　Child Return £9.00 (Under-3s free)
　　　　　Family Return £45.00 (2 Adult + 2 Child)
　　　　　Senior Citizen Return £15.00
Note: Extra discounts are available for large groups.

E-mail: trains@southdevonrailway.org

Detailed Directions by Car:
Buckfastleigh is half way between Exeter and Plymouth on the A38 Devon Expressway. Totnes can be reached by taking the A385 from Paignton and Torquay. Brown tourist signs give directions for the railway.

SPA VALLEY RAILWAY

Address: West Station, Tunbridge Wells, Kent TN2 5QY **Telephone Nº**: (01892) 537715 or 300141 **Year Formed**: 1985 **Location of Line**: Tunbridge Wells West to Groombridge and Eridge **Length**: 5 miles	**Nº of Steam Locos**: 7 **Nº of Other Locos**: 8 + 3 DMUs **Nº of Members**: Approximately 1,000 **Annual Membership Fee**: £20.00 **Approx Nº of Visitors P.A.**: 42,000 **Gauge**: Standard **Web Site**: www.spavalleyrailway.co.uk

GENERAL INFORMATION

Nearest Mainline Station: Eridge (cross-platform interchange with the mainline)
Nearest Bus Stop: Outside Sainsbury's (100yds)
Car Parking: Available in Tunbridge Wells nearby in Major Yorks Road, Union House & Linden Close
Coach Parking: Montacute Road (150 yards)
Souvenir Shop(s): Yes   **Food & Drinks**: Yes

SPECIAL INFORMATION

The Railway's Tunbridge Wells Terminus is in a historic and unique L.B. & S.C.R. engine shed. The extension to Eridge is now open at weekends and on public holidays and tickets inclusive of entry to Groombridge Place Gardens are also available.

OPERATING INFORMATION

Opening Times: 2019 dates: Weekends and Bank Holidays, March to October inclusive. Tuesday to Thursday during the School Holidays. Thursdays from June to the beginning of September. Santa Specials run from 29th to 31st December and also on 1st January 2019.
Steam Working: Services alternate between steam and diesel haulage. Trains run from 10.20am to 3.20pm though this may vary during special events.
Prices: Adult Return £12.00   Child Return £7.00
Senior Citizen Return £11.00
Family Return £30.00 (2 adult + 2 child)
Fares vary on some special event days.
Fares allow unlimited travel on the day of issue except for special event days.

Detailed Directions by Car:
The Spa Valley Railway is in the southern part of Tunbridge Wells, 100 yards off the A26. Tunbridge Wells Station is adjacent to Sainsbury's and Homebase.   For Eridge Station (Satnav TN3 9LE), follow signs off the A26.

STEAM – MUSEUM OF THE GREAT WESTERN RAILWAY

Address: STEAM – Museum of the Great Western Railway, Firefly Avenue, Swindon SN2 2EY
Telephone Nº: (01793) 466646
Year Formed: 2000

Nº of Steam Locos: 8
Nº of Other Locos: 1
Approx Nº of Visitors P.A.: 100,000
Web site: www.steam-museum.org.uk
E-mail: adminsteam@swindon.gov.uk

GENERAL INFORMATION

Nearest Mainline Station: Swindon (10 min. walk)
Nearest Bus Station: Swindon (10 minute walk)
Car Parking: Ample parking space available in the Outlet Centre (charges apply)
Coach Parking: Free parking on site and nearby
Souvenir Shop(s): Yes
Food & Drinks: There is a Café within the Museum

SPECIAL INFORMATION

STEAM tells the story of the men and women who built the Great Western Railway.

OPERATING INFORMATION

Opening Times: Open daily all year round from 11.00am to 5.00pm (4.00pm on Sundays. Last admission is 4.00pm (3.00pm on Sundays). Closed from 24th to 26th December.
Steam Working: During some special events only – please check the Museum web site for details.
Prices: Adult Tickets £9.35
            Child Tickets £6.95
            Family Tickets £16.30 to £34.65
            Senior Citizen Tickets £7.50
            Children under 3 are admitted free
Note: Season tickets are also available and prices for Special Events may be higher.

Detailed Directions by Car:
Exit the M4 at Junction 16 and follow the brown tourist signs to 'Outlet Centre'. Similarly follow the brown signs from all other major routes.   From the Railway Station: STEAM is a 10 to 15 minute walk and is accessible through the pedestrian tunnel – entrance by Emlyn Square.

THE STRATHSPEY RAILWAY

Address: Aviemore Station, Dalfaber Road, Aviemore PH22 1PY	**Nº of Steam Locos:** 7 (2 in service)
Telephone Nº: (01479) 810725	**Nº of Other Locos:** 10
Year Formed: 1971	**Nº of Members:** 900
Location of Line: Aviemore to Boat of Garten and Broomhill, Inverness-shire	**Annual Membership Fee:** £24.00
	Approx Nº of Visitors P.A.: 81,000
	Gauge: Standard
Length of Line: 9½ miles at present	**Web site:** www.strathspeyrailway.co.uk

GENERAL INFORMATION

Nearest Mainline Station: Aviemore – Strathspey trains depart from Platform 3
Nearest Bus Station: Aviemore (adjacent)
Car Parking: Available at all stations
Coach Parking: Available at Aviemore and Broomhill stations
Souvenir Shop(s): Yes – at all stations
Food & Drinks: Available on most services

SPECIAL INFORMATION

Experience the stunning Scottish Highlands in a way like no other as the Railway wends its way through the stunning Cairngorm Mountains.

OPERATING INFORMATION

Opening Times: 2019 dates: Daily in July and August. Weekends from 30th March to 27th October. Wednesday & Thursday in April, May, June, September and October. Fridays in June and September and other dates in February and March. Winter Specials operate on dates in December and January. Please phone for details. Generally open from 10.30am to 4.30pm.
Steam Working: Most trains are steam-hauled but special diesel services are timetabled throughout the year. Please check the web site for further details.
Prices: Adult Return £15.75
　　　　　Child Return £7.90 (Under-5s free)
　　　　　Senior Citizen Return £14.15
Note: Day Rover tickets are also available.

Detailed Directions by Car:
For Aviemore Station from South: Take the A9 then B970 and turn left between the railway & river bridges. For Boat of Garten from North; Take the A9 then A938 to Carr Bridge, then B9153 and A95 and follow the signs; From North East: Take A95 to Boat of Garten or Broomhill (3½ miles South from Grantown-on-Spey).

SWANAGE RAILWAY

Address: Station House, Railway Station, Swanage, Dorset BH19 1HB	**No of Steam Locos**: 10 (3 in service)
	No of Other Locos: 6
Telephone No: (01929) 425800	**No of Members**: 4,200
Year Formed: 1976	**Annual Membership Fee**: Adult £21.00;
Location of Line: Swanage to Norden	Junior £12.00; Family £42.00
Length of Line: 6 miles	**Approx No of Visitors P.A.**: 216,000
Gauge: Standard	**Web site**: www.swanagerailway.co.uk

GENERAL INFORMATION

Nearest Mainline Station: Wareham (10 miles)
Nearest Bus Station: Swanage Station (adjacent)
Car Parking: Park & Ride at Norden. Public car parks in Swanage (5 minutes walk)
Coach Parking: Available at Norden
Souvenir Shop(s): Yes – at Swanage Station
Food & Drinks: Yes – buffet available on trains and also Swanage Station Buffet and at Norden.

SPECIAL INFORMATION

The railway runs along part of the route of the old Swanage to Wareham railway, opened in 1885.

OPERATING INFORMATION

Opening Times: 2019 dates: Weekends from 16th February until the end of the year then daily from 22nd March to 3rd November (but closed on 14th, 18th, 21st & 25th October). Also open on a number of other dates throughout the year including Santa Specials in December. Usually open from 10.00am to around 5.00pm although trains may run later from May to September and evening services operate during some dates in the school summer holidays.
Steam Working: Most services are steam-hauled. Please check with the Railway for further details.
Prices: Adult Return £15.00   Child Return £8.00
             Family Ticket £39.00
Note: Prices shown above are the maximum return fares and may be subject to change.

Detailed Directions by Car:
Norden Park & Ride Station is situated off the A351 on the approach to Corfe Castle. Swanage Station is situated in the centre of the town, just a few minutes walk from the beach. Take the A351 to reach Swanage.

SWINDON & CRICKLADE RAILWAY

Address: Blunsdon Station, Tadpole Lane, Blunsdon, Swindon, Wilts SN25 2DA	**Nº of Steam Locos**: 6
	Nº of Other Locos: 9
Phone Nº: (01793) 771615	**Nº of Members**: 600
Year Formed: 1978	**Annual Membership Fee**: £15.00
Location: Mouldon Hill to Hayes Knoll	**Approx Nº of Visitors P.A.**: 16,000
Length of Line: 2½ miles	**Gauge**: Standard

Photo by Pete Todd

GENERAL INFORMATION

Nearest Mainline Station: Swindon (5 miles)
Nearest Bus Station: Bus stop at Oakhurst (¾ mile)
Car Parking: Free parking at Blunsdon Station
Coach Parking: Free parking at Blunsdon Station
Souvenir Shop(s): Yes
Food & Drinks: Yes

SPECIAL INFORMATION

The Engine Shed at Hayes Knoll Station is occasionally open to the public.

Web site: www.swindon-cricklade-railway.org

OPERATING INFORMATION

Opening Times: 2019 dates: The Railway is open every weekend and Bank Holiday from Easter to late November. Also on Wednesdays in July and August and Sundays in November. Santa Specials run in December and other various special events throughout the year also have Steam train rides. Open 10.30am to 4.00pm.
Steam Working: Every Sunday from Easter until the end of October and certain other dates – please contact the railway for further details.
Prices: Adult £8.00   Child £6.00
          Concessions £7.00   Family £24.00
Prices are different for Special Event days.

Detailed Directions by Car:
From the M4: Exit the M4 at Junction 15 and follow the A419. Turn left towards Blunsdon Stadium and follow the signs for the Railway: From Cirencester: Follow the A419 to the top of Blunsdon Hill, then turn right and follow signs for Blundson Stadium.

TANFIELD RAILWAY

Address: Marley Hill Engine Shed, Old Marley Hill, Gateshead, Tyne & Wear NE16 5ET	**No of Steam Locos**: 29 Standard, 2 Narrow
	No Other Locos: 12 Standard, 15 Narrow
	No of Members: 150
Telephone No: 0750 809-2365	**Annual Membership Fee**: £12.00 (Adult)
Year Formed: 1976	**Approx No of Visitors P.A.**: 40,000
Location of Line: Between Sunniside & East Tanfield, Co. Durham	**Gauge**: Standard and Narrow gauge
	Web site: www.tanfield-railway.co.uk
Length of Line: 3 miles	

GENERAL INFORMATION

Nearest Mainline Station: Newcastle-upon-Tyne (8 miles)
Nearest Bus St'n: Gateshead Interchange (6 miles)
Car Parking: Spaces for 150 cars at Andrews House and 100 spaces at East Tanfield
Coach Parking: Spaces for 6 or 7 coaches only
Souvenir Shop(s): Yes
Food & Drinks: Yes – light snacks only

SPECIAL INFORMATION

Tanfield Railway is the oldest existing railway in use – it was originally opened in 1725. It also runs beside The Causey Arch, the oldest railway bridge in the world.

OPERATING INFORMATION

Opening Times: Every Sunday & Bank Holiday Monday throughout the year. Also open on Thursdays and Saturdays during the Summer school holidays and for other events throughout the year. Santa Specials run on weekends and other dates in December and November.
Steam Working: Most trains are steam-hauled and run from 10.30am to 3.30pm (from 10.30am to 3.00pm during the Winter months).
Prices: Adult £10.50
 Child £6.50 (Under 5's travel free)
 Senior Citizen £8.50
 Family £27.50 (2 adults + 2 children)
Note: Special Event days may have higher prices.

Detailed Directions by Car:
Sunniside Station is off the A6076 Sunniside to Stanley road in Co. Durham. To reach the Railway, leave A1(M), follow signs for Beamish museum at Chester-le-Street then continue to Stanley and follow Tanfield Railway signs.

TELFORD STEAM RAILWAY

Address: The Old Loco Shed, Bridge Road, Horsehay, Telford, Shropshire TF4 3UH
Telephone Enquiries: (01952) 503880
Year Formed: 1976
Location: Horsehay & Dawley Station
Length of Line: 1 mile standard gauge, an eighth of a mile 2 foot narrow gauge

Nº of Steam Locos: 5 (2 operational)
Nº of Other Locos: 11
Nº of Members: Approximately 220
Annual Membership Fee: £20.00 Adult
Approx Nº of Visitors P.A.: 10,000
Web site: www.telfordsteamrailway.co.uk

GENERAL INFORMATION

Nearest Mainline Station: Wellington or Telford Central
Nearest Bus Station: Dawley (1 mile)
Car Parking: Free parking at the site
Coach Parking: Free parking at the site
Souvenir Shop(s): 'Freight Stop Gift Shop'
Food & Drinks: 'The Furnaces' Tea Room

SPECIAL INFORMATION

Telford Steam Railway has both a Standard Gauge and Narrow Gauge line as well as Miniature and Model Railways. A major extension to the line has recently opened.

OPERATING INFORMATION

Opening Times: 2019 dates: Every Sunday and Bank Holiday between 20th April and 29th September. Santa Specials operate on dates during December. Open 11.00am to 4.30pm.
Steam Working: Most Bank Holidays. Please contact the railway for further information.
Prices: Adult all day tickets £7.00
Child all day tickets £5.00
Concession all day tickets £5.00
Family all day tickets £18.00
(2 adults + 3 children)
Note: Higher prices apply for special event days and season tickets are available.

Detailed Directions by Car:
From All Parts: Exit the M54 at Junction 6, travel south along the A5223 then follow the brown tourist signs for the railway. Note: If using a SatNav please enter TF4 2NF as the destination postcode.

THE WEARDALE RAILWAY

Address: Stanhope Station, Stanhope, Bishop Auckland DL13 2YS **Telephone Nº**: (01388) 526203 **Year Formed**: 1993 **Location**: Stanhope to Bishop Auckland **Length of Line**: 18 miles	**Nº of Steam Locos**: 1 **Nº of Other Locos**: 4 (including DMUs) **Nº of Members**: 850 **Gauge**: Standard **Web site**: www.weardale-railway.org.uk

GENERAL INFORMATION

Nearest Mainline Station: Bishop Auckland (¼ mile)
Nearest Bus Station: Bishop Auckland
Car Parking: Available at both Stanhope and Wolsingham Stations
Coach Parking: Available at Wolsingham Station
Souvenir Shop(s): Yes
Food & Drinks: Yes – Signal Box Cafe, Stanhope

SPECIAL INFORMATION

Weardale is in the heart of the North Pennines and the railway provides magnificent unspoilt views. The area is known for its footpaths and bridleways and the railway provides a useful base for walks between stations along banks of the beautiful River Wear.

OPERATING INFORMATION

Opening Times: 2019 heritage rail services will operate on weekends and bank holidays from 23rd March to 3rd November. Services will also operate on Wednesdays and Thursdays from 3rd July to 11th September. Also open on weekends and other selected days in December. Please check the web site for further information when planning a visit. Trains run from 10.00am to 3.00pm.
Steam Working: None at present.
Prices: Adult Return £16.00
         Child Return £9.00 (Under-5s free)
         Concession Return £14.00
         Family Return £41.00 (2 Adult + 3 Child)
Note: The prices shown above are for a return journey from Stanhope to Bishop Auckland and may be subject to change.

Detailed Directions by Car:
From All Parts: Stanhope Station is located in Stanhope, just off the A689; Bishop Auckland West Station is a short walk from the Northern Rail Mainline Station in Bishop Auckland (SatNavs use DL14 7TL).

WENSLEYDALE RAILWAY

Address: Leeming Bar Station, Leases Road, Leeming Bar, Northallerton DL7 9AR	**Nº of Steam Locos:** Visiting locos only
Telephone Nº: (01677) 425805	**Nº of Other Locos:** 10 + 2 DMUs
Year Formed: The railway association was formed in 1990, the Railway PLC in 2000.	**Nº of Members:** 3,500
	Annual Membership Fee: £17.50
Location of Line: Leeming Bar to Redmire	**Approx Nº of Visitors P.A.:** Not known
Length of Line: Approximately 16 miles	**Gauge:** Standard
	Web site: www.wensleydalerail.com

GENERAL INFORMATION

Nearest Mainline Station: Northallerton (7 miles)
Nearest Bus Station: Northallerton (7 miles)
Car & Coach Parking: Available at Leeming Bar, Leyburn and Redmire Stations
Souvenir Shop(s): Yes
Food & Drinks: At Leeming Bar, Bedale & Leyburn stations.

SPECIAL INFORMATION

Most services are operated via DMU and travel to Leyburn & Redmire tourist destinations in the Wensleydale Valley. Other heritage diesel groups also use the line.

OPERATING INFORMATION

Opening Times: 2019 dates: Weekends and Bank Holidays from 9th February to end of November. Tuesdays and most Wednesdays from 16th April to the end of September. Open daily in August (but for Mondays and Thursdays when the railway is closed). A limited timetable operates on weekends in November. Also open for a number of other Special Event Days including Santa Specials in December. Please contact the railway for further information.
Steam Working: Most services are operated by DMU except during the summer months when a visiting steam locomotive should be in operation.
Prices: A variety of single and Day Ticket fares are available at both standard and discounted rates. Please contact the railway for further details.

Detailed Directions by Car:
From All Parts: Exit the A1 at the Leeming Bar exit and take the A684 towards Northallerton. The station is on the left after about ¼ mile close to the road junction and after the traffic lights.   By Bus: The Dales & District 73 bus route travels between Northallerton and Leeming Bar.

WEST SOMERSET RAILWAY

Address: The Railway Station, Minehead, Somerset TA24 5BG	**Nº of Steam Locos:** 6 **Other Locos:** 9
Telephone Nº: (01643) 704996 (enquiries)	**Nº of Members:** 3,500
Year Formed: 1976	**Annual Membership Fee:** £25.00
Location: Bishops Lydeard to Minehead	**Approx Nº of Visitors P.A.:** 200,000
Length of Line: 19¾ miles	**Gauge:** Standard
	Web site: www.west-somerset-railway.co.uk

GENERAL INFORMATION

Nearest Mainline Station: Taunton (4 miles)
Nearest Bus Station: Taunton (4½ miles) – Service 28 run to Bishops Lydeard, Watchet, Washford and Minehead.
Car Parking: Available at all stations except Doniford Halt. Free parking at Bishops Lydeard.
Coach Parking: As above
Souvenir Shops: Yes – at Minehead, Bishops Lydeard and Washford. Sales counters at other stations.
Food & Drinks: Yes – At some stations. Buffet cars on most trains.

SPECIAL INFORMATION

Britain's longest Standard gauge Heritage railway runs through the Quantock Hills and along the Bristol Channel Coast. The line passes through no fewer than ten Stations with museums at Washford and Blue Anchor and a turntable at Minehead.

OPERATING INFORMATION

Opening Times: 2019 dates: Daily from 30th March to 2nd November but closed most Mondays & Fridays in April & October and most Fridays in May. Santa Specials run on weekends and other dates in December. Open 10.00am to 5.00pm. Please contact the railway for details.
Steam Working: All operating days except during Diesel Galas.
Prices: Adult Day Rover £22.00
Child Day Rover £11.00 (ages 3 to 17)
Family Rover £55.00 (2 adult + 2 child)
Senior Citizen Day Rover £21.00
Note: Tickets purchased in advance are cheaper

Detailed Directions by Car:
Exit the M5 at Taunton (Junction 25) and follow the A358 towards Minehead. Bishops Lydeard Station is signposted from the village bypass. The A39 (which the A358 joins at Williton) goes directly past Washford Station. Minehead Station is on the seafront at the edge of the town centre, approximately ½ miles from Butlins Holiday Centre.

WHITWELL & REEPHAM RAILWAY

Address: Whitwell Road, Reepham, Norfolk NR10 4GA	**Nº of Steam Locos:** 2 **Other Locos:** 4
Telephone Nº: (01603) 871694	**Nº of Members:** Approximately 400
Year Formed: 2009	**Annual Membership Fee:** £15.00
Location of Line: Norfolk	**Approx Nº of Visitors P.A.:** 20,000
Length of Line: 1 mile	**Gauge:** Standard
	Web site: www.whitwellstation.com

GENERAL INFORMATION

Nearest Mainline Station: Norwich (15 miles)
Nearest Bus Station: Norwich (15 miles)
Car Parking: Available on site
Coach Parking: Available
Souvenir Shop(s): Yes
Food & Drinks: Available in 'The Sidings' café bar

SPECIAL INFORMATION

Whitwell & Reepham Railway celebrated 10th years of operation on 28th February 2019, coinciding almost exactly with the 60th anniversary of the closure of the Midland & Great Northern railway on 2nd March 1959. The Society has restored the station, relaid track and sidings and acquired more rolling stock. The station is preserved as a museum, ticket office and shop with a further museum, 7¼ inch light railway and 'The Sidings' a purpose-built café, bar and function room also on site.

OPERATING INFORMATION

Opening Times: Open for static viewing daily throughout the year from 10.00am until 5.00pm. Diesel services run at weekends throughout the year except when Steam trains are running. Please check the railway's web site for further details.
Steam Working: The first Sunday of each month plus a number of other Special Event days. Please contact the railway for further details. Steam services operate from 12.30pm to 4.00pm.
Prices: Adults £3.00   Children £1.00
     Family £7.00
Note: Prices shown above are for train rides – admission to the museum is free except during the Steam Rally held in the first week in August.

Detailed Directions by Car:
From All Parts: Take the A1067 Norwich to Fakenham Road to Bawdeswell then follow the B1145 to Reepham. The railway is located about 1 mile to the South-west of Reepham and is well-signposted.

YEOVIL RAILWAY CENTRE

Address: Yeovil Junction Station, Stoford, Yeovil BA22 9UU	**No of Steam Locos:** 2
Telephone No: (01935) 410420	**No of Other Locos:** 3
Year Formed: 1994	**No of Members:** 300
Location of Line: Yeovil Junction	**Annual Membership Fee:** £15.00
Length of Line: ¼ mile	**Approx No of Visitors P.A.:** 5,000
Gauge: Standard	**Web site:** www.yeovilrailway.freeservers.com

GENERAL INFORMATION

Nearest Mainline Station: Yeovil Junction (adjacent)
Nearest Bus Station: A regular bus service runs Monday to Saturday from Yeovil Bus Station (2 miles)
Car Parking: Available on site
Coach Parking: Available nearby
Souvenir Shop(s): Yes
Food & Drinks: Available

SPECIAL INFORMATION

The Visitor Centre is located in a GWR Transfer Shed which was built in 1864. The centre also runs Driver Experience days and Peckett steam engine 'Pectin' returns to service in 2019.

OPERATING INFORMATION

Opening Times: Open regularly for Steam Train days, Mainline steam visits and other special events from March to October. Also open for Santa Specials in December and for static viewing every Sunday morning from 10.00am until noon. Please contact the Centre for further details of event days.
Steam Working: Numerous operating days throughout the year. Please contact the Centre for further details.
Prices: Adult £8.00
Child £4.00 (Ages 5 to 15)
One child is admitted free with each paying adult
Note: Prices shown above are for Steam Working days.

Detailed Directions by Car:
The Centre is part of Yeovil Junction Station which is served by South Western Railway. By road simply follow the signs to Yeovil Junction Station from Yeovil town centre or from the A37 Dorchester to Yeovil road. The entrance to Yeovil Railway Centre is through the low bridge, half way up the Yeovil Junction Station approach road.